THE TWELVE LAB〜 〜ᴏꜰ HERCULES

Born with both a curse and a
blessing from the Gods, Hercules
led a life of superhuman
adventure. In this vigorous
retelling, Robert Newman
brings to modern readers one of
the greatest and most exciting of
the ancient Greek hero tales.

'You must go to the man you
dislike most in the world and
perform twelve labours that he
will set for you.' So commanded
the Oracle; and Hercules, anxious
to atone for a crime he had
committed, knew he must obey.
He could not marry his beloved
Megara until the gods had
forgiven him and his own
conscience was cleared. But the
tasks set him by King
Eurystheus were the most
difficult and dangerous
imaginable.

Charles Keeping, winner of the
Kate Greenaway Award, has
interpreted the text with
powerful illustrations that
perfectly match the heroic
proportions of this ancient tale.

The Twelve Labours of Hercules

Told by ROBERT NEWMAN

Illustrated by Charles Keeping

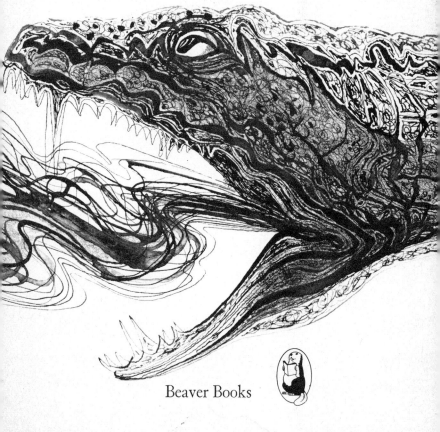

Beaver Books

First published in Great Britain in 1973 by
Hutchinson Junior Books Limited
3 Fitzroy Square, London W1

This paperback edition published in 1976 by
The Hamlyn Publishing Group Limited
London · New York · Sydney · Toronto
Astronaut House, Feltham, Middlesex, England
Reprinted 1976

© Copyright Text Robert Newman 1972
© Copyright Illustrations Charles Keeping 1972

ISBN 0 600 38737 2

Printed in England by
Hazell Watson & Viney Limited, Aylesbury, Bucks

Cover illustration by Pat Owen

CONTENTS

Appropriately, for JOAN

I

THE
BIRTH OF
HERCULES

Zeus, supreme ruler of the gods, sat on his throne on Mount Olympus waiting for the birth of another of his earthly children. He had been the father of many sons and many daughters, both in heaven and on earth. But this son—born not of an immortal but of an earthly mother—was to be the greatest of them all, the strongest and bravest of men and the greatest hero of his time.

Zeus waved his hand, and the clouds that shrouded Olympus parted so that he could look down on the city of Thebes where Alcmene, wife of exiled King Amphitryon, was beginning her labour. Some nine months before, shortly after Amphitryon had been banished from Mycenae, he had left his wife briefly to lead his army in battle. While he was away Zeus had assumed his shape and come to Alcmene during the night so that neither she nor her husband realized that the child she was about to have was more than human.

It was at this moment, while Zeus watched the comings and goings in the palace at Thebes, that his wife, Hera, approached him.

"I gather that another child of yours is about to be born down there on earth," she said.

"A son. His name will be Hercules."

"Since he is your son, I suspect that you have great plans for him."

"He will be a great hero," said Zeus, "whose fame will echo throughout Greece. Not only that, but although he will be born in exile he will rule the House of Perseus and be the High King of Mycenae."

"Will he be born soon?"

"Before nightfall."

"In other words, the prince of the House of Perseus who is born before nightfall will be the High King."

Zeus, distracted by a sudden earthquake in Crete—the work of his brother Poseidon, the Earth-shaker—nodded.

"That is what I said."

"And what you say is fixed and unchangeable," said Hera. "Thank you, noble Zeus."

Now Hera had always been jealous of any of Zeus' children who were not hers, and she was determined, in this case at least, to bring his plans to naught. It happened that at that same time the wife of the High King of Mycenae was also carrying a child. Though it was not due to be born for another two months, Hera brought on the queen's labour early. Then, assuming the form of a witch, she hurried to Thebes and squatted cross-legged before Alcmene's door with her clothing tied in knots and her fingers locked together. By this magic she delayed the birth of Hercules until after the sun had set.

Thus it was that when the gods gathered in the great hall of Olympus shortly after dusk, Hermes, the messenger of the gods, appeared and said, "I bring news, mighty Zeus. A royal son has been born to the House of Perseus."

"Hercules," said Zeus.

"No," said Hermes, somewhat awkwardly. "He was born to Nicippe, wife of the King of Mycenae, and his name is Eurystheus."

"What?" roared Zeus. Again he looked down at Thebes, where, by the light of flaring torches, Alcmene was at last giving birth to Hercules.

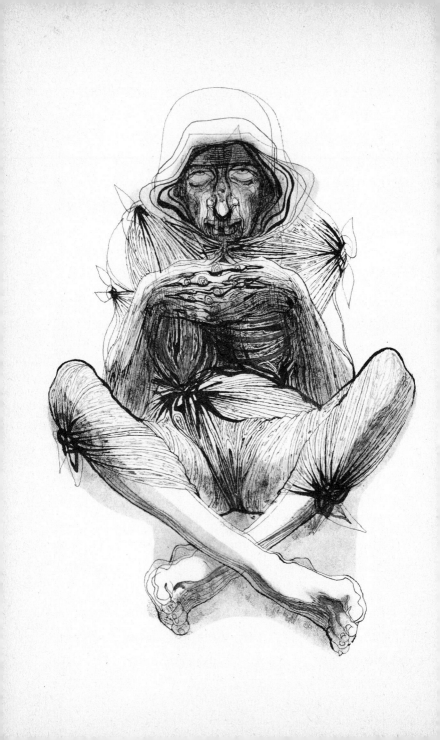

"This is your doing!" he said furiously to Hera.

"Mine?" said Hera, with pretended meekness. "What is my power compared to yours, noble Zeus?"

"Your power is as nothing, but your spite and deceit are boundless! But hear this. Though you have tricked me and denied my son his birthright, there is that which you cannot deny him. While Eurystheus shall be the High King, his name will be forgotten in time to come. But Hercules will perform deeds so glorious that his name will be remembered forever. And when his work on earth is done, he shall join us here on Olympus and become a god like us."

"Zeus has spoken," said Hermes. "Hear him, O white-robed Fates, spinners of the lives of men. Hear and obey!"

2

THE
YOUTH
OF HERCULES

Amphitryon, Alcmene's husband, was overjoyed that his firstborn child was a son. And not realizing that Hera was the child's sworn enemy, he named him in her honour, calling him Heracles, or Hercules, which means Glory of Hera. His joy was soon doubled, for shortly after midnight Alcmene gave birth to a second son, Hercules' twin, whom they named Iphicles.

Both Hercules and Iphicles were strong, healthy babies. And though, from the time he was born, Hercules was always the larger and stronger, no one realized just how extraordinary he was until both children were a year old. Hera had been watching Hercules jealously, and one night, when Zeus was feasting in the great hall with the other gods, she sent two enormous serpents to destroy this son of her husband.

The huge snakes, with sky-blue scales and flaming eyes, approached the gates of the palace. At Hera's command the gates opened and the serpents glided through the corridors to the room where the twins lay sleeping. They both awoke. Iphicles, seeing the two great serpents writhing above them, screamed in terror and rolled off the shield that was their cradle. But without a sound Hercules reached up and seized the serpents by the throat, one with his right hand and one with his left.

Roused by Iphicles' frightened cries, Amphitryon ran into the room with a torch and a drawn sword. Raising the torch high, he paused in astonishment. Hercules, smiling, was holding out to him the limp bodies of the two serpents—the serpents he had strangled, one with each hand.

In the morning Amphitryon called in the most famous soothsayer in Greece. He was old and blind, and his name was Teiresias. The soothsayer listened to the tale of what had happened during the night and advised Amphitryon to burn the bodies of the serpents on the high altar as a sacrifice to Zeus. It was clear, he said, that Zeus had been the child's protector.

"It is also clear," he said, "that he is no ordinary child but is destined to be a hero. In fact, I prophesy that he will be the greatest hero Greece has ever known."

When the twins were old enough, Amphitryon began training them in the arts of war, calling in the most famous warriors of Greece to help him. The two boys learned to wrestle and box, to drive a chariot, and to use the sword, the javelin, and the bow. And though Iphicles soon became very skilful in all these, Hercules not only surpassed him, but, by the time he was eighteen, surpassed even his masters in all the warlike arts, even as he surpassed them and all other men in strength and courage.

Now that Hercules was full-grown he was anxious to prove himself in some sort of adventure. In spite of Teiresias' prophecy, Alcmene had a mother's fears about this. But Amphitryon, a famous warrior himself, gave him leave to go and do what he would.

There was a savage lion that lived in the hills to the south. The lion had been attacking the Theban cattle and those belonging to King Thespius, ruler of the neighbouring kingdom. Hercules tracked it to its lair, and scorning to use his bow, sword, or javelin on a mere beast, killed it with a club he had cut from a wild-olive tree. He brought the lion's skin to King Thespius, telling him the beast would trouble him no more, and the king thanked him, saying Hercules should call on him if he ever needed a friend.

As Hercules was returning to Thebes, striding up the middle of the road with his club over his shoulder, he was overtaken by a group of chariots, each driven by a warrior—the armed guard of a richly dressed herald. The driver of the leading chariot arrogantly ordered Hercules out of the way, but leaning on his club, Hercules asked who he was and where the party was going.

"If you live in these parts and don't know, you must be even more dull-witted than you look," said the warrior. "We are from Orchomenus and we are on our way to Thebes to collect our yearly tribute."

Hercules knew about the tribute and had always resented it. When he was only a small boy, he had heard about the ill-fated chariot race in which the son of King Creon of Thebes had fatally injured the King of Orchomenus. Before he died, the king made his son, Erginus, swear to avenge him. Erginus had immediately marched on Thebes, conquered it, and forced Creon to agree to pay a yearly tribute of a hundred cattle.

"I may be dull-witted," said Hercules, "but I am

not as lily-livered as the Thebans for continuing to pay you tribute. If it were up to me, I would pay you in a very different way."

"Ride him down," ordered the herald.

Lashing his horses, the driver of the leading chariot came thundering down on Hercules. But Hercules was able to seize the horses by their reins and check them. Then, knocking the charioteer unconscious with his club, he turned the horses and sent them careering back the way they had come. He served several of the other chariots in the same way, and the rest of the drivers fled.

Hercules continued on his way to Thebes, where he was warmly greeted by his parents. He told them of his adventure with the lion, but said nothing about his meeting with the herald and warriors of King Erginus. A few days later, however, Erginus sent another herald to Thebes, demanding that—in addition to the tribute —King Creon surrender for punishment the youth who had attacked and insulted his emissaries.

Creon knew that this must have been Hercules, and when he sent for him, Hercules freely admitted that he had been responsible.

"Then," said Creon, "much as I dislike it, I must send you to Erginus along with the tribute, and I can only hope that he will not be too hard on you."

"Why?" asked Hercules. "And why do you continue to pay tribute instead of fighting Erginus?"

"Though you are not a Theban," said Creon, "you were born here and you should know the answer to that. When Erginus conquered us he seized all our arms and forbade our young men to learn to use them. This did not apply to you and your brother since you were strangers living among us. But you and he are the only youths who could strike a blow against Erginus."

"I believe that the young men of Thebes know more about the use of arms than you think," said Hercules. "As for weapons, I have seen many of them in the temples."

He was talking about the spoils of earlier and more successful wars, which had been dedicated to the gods.

"But we cannot touch them," said Creon. "They belong to the gods."

"I don't think the gods would mind our using them if we used them well," said Hercules. "When must you send me to Erginus?"

"He said if you and the tribute were not in Orchomenus in thirty days, he would come and get you—and it."

"Will you let me give him Thebes' answer?" asked Hercules. "And will you let me give it where and when I think best?"

Creon thought about this, studying the tall, strong, still beardless youth who stood before him. Then, remembering Teiresias' prophecy, he nodded.

"Yes, Hercules," he said.

"Good," said Hercules. "You will not be sorry."

He had already talked to all the young men of Thebes, and now, leaving Creon's palace, he led them into the temple of Zeus. The walls of the temple were covered with armour and weapons—swords, spears, shields, and breastplates—that had been captured in wars long past and placed there as offerings.

"Father Zeus," said Hercules, standing before the high altar, "you know our need. Is it your will that we use these weapons? If it is, give us a sign."

Though the sky was cloudless, there was a sudden, distant rumble of thunder that shook the temple, and a great spear hanging over the altar fell from its place into Hercules' hand.

"Thank you, Father Zeus," said Hercules, raising the spear in salute. He nodded to the young men and they immediately began arming themselves with the weapons of all the temples in Thebes.

During the days that followed, Hercules and his twin brother, Iphicles, trained the young Thebans in the use of arms and taught them to fight in formation. On the thirtieth day, Hercules led them to a narrow pass a few miles from Thebes and hid them on the high ground on either side of it. About noon Erginus and his army appeared, driving their chariots toward Thebes. Hercules waited until they were well into the pass; then, rising to his feet, he called, "Stay, Erginus. Where are you going?"

"Are you from Thebes?" asked Erginus.

"I am."

"I have waited for thirty days for Creon to send me the insolent young upstart who attacked my emissaries. Since he has not done so, I have come for him myself."

"Then I can save you at least part of your journey," said Hercules. "I am the man you want."

"Take him," ordered Erginus. As he spoke, Hercules cast his spear. It flew straight and with such force that it not only slew Erginus, but also killed the captain who drove his chariot. Then with a shout, Hercules ran down the hill with his warriors behind him.

The battle did not last long. Taken by surprise, and with their king and captain slain, the men of Orchomenus broke and fled. Hercules and his band followed hard on their heels, battered down the city gates, and forced the people of Orchomenus not only to surrender, but to pay back to Thebes the entire amount of the tribute that Thebes had paid to the city.

3

THE
MADNESS
OF HERCULES

Hercules and his brother, Iphicles, returned in triumph to Thebes. They were met at the gates by Creon, who praised and thanked them and in reward for what they had done offered them his daughters in marriage. Now Hercules had long been in love with Megara, Creon's oldest daughter, a tall, golden-haired maiden. But he told Creon he would not marry her until Thebes was truly safe. For he suspected that the people of Orchomenus would not accept their unexpected defeat but would attack Thebes again. So, when Iphicles married Creon's younger daughter a few days later, Hercules and Megara attended the ceremony as guests rather than as a second bridal couple.

During the next year Hercules continued to train the Theban army and also cleared the land of bandits and evildoers. Near the end of that time a son was born to Iphicles, and whenever Hercules returned to Thebes from one of his expeditions, he would play with his infant nephew and dream of the time when he and Megara would have sons like him.

Finally, as Hercules had expected, the people of Orchomenus sent another army against Thebes. This time they were joined by their allies, the Euboeans, and they far outnumbered the Thebans. But led by Hercules and Iphicles, the Thebans routed them completely, and this time Hercules made the Kings of Orchomenus and Euboea swear solemn oaths that they would never attack Thebes again.

Now preparations were made for the marriage of Hercules and Megara. Guests began pouring into Thebes for this joyous occasion, for young though he was, Hercules was already a famous hero. But Hera, who was more jealous of Hercules than ever because of this fame, was determined to prevent his marriage. The night before it was to take place, she sent a madness to Hercules in the form of a high fever.

Awakened at midnight by the arrival of more guests, and believing, in his delirium, that Thebes was again being attacked, Hercules ran out into the court-

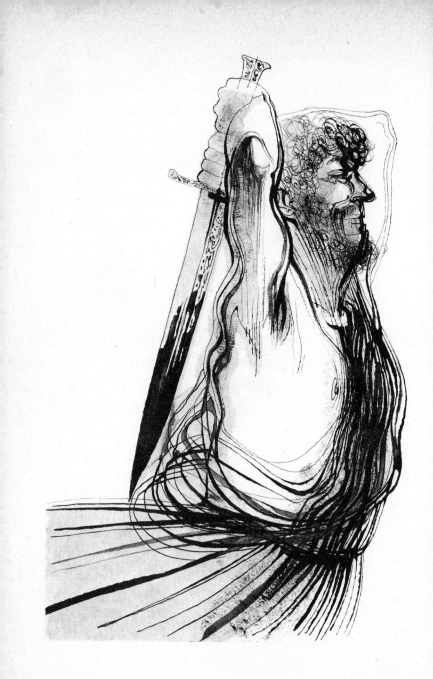

yard and began laying about him with his sword. The madness left as suddenly as it had come. Looking down at the bodies of those he had slain, Hercules moaned in horror, dropped his sword, and fled from the city.

For months he roamed the hills and forests, living on nuts and berries and avoiding all who sought him. One morning, however, he awoke to see his brother, Iphicles, standing before him.

"Come no closer," said Hercules. "Do not touch me. My hands are covered with blood."

"We have shared everything before this," said his brother. "Why should I not share your guilt?"

"Because I will not have it," said Hercules. "I have committed one of the greatest of all crimes—I have slain guests within my own house."

"It was not you who slew them," said Iphicles. "It was a madman who did not know what he was doing. I am not a king or a priest, so I cannot purify you. But there is one not far from here who can."

"Who is that?" asked Hercules.

"Your friend, King Thespius, for whom you slew the lion. Come there with me."

"I do not believe any mortal can purify me. But I will go with you."

Together they went to King Thespius, who performed the rites of purification. "But," he told Hercules, "I cannot give you the penance that will cleanse you completely of your guilt. The gods must do that."

"That is my thought also," said Hercules. "What, then, shall I do?"

"Go to Delphi and consult the Pythoness, for she speaks with the voice of Apollo."

So Hercules went north to Delphi, and entering the temple of Apollo, told the priests he wished to consult the oracle. They made him fast for three days, speaking to no one during that time and sleeping on the ground in the grove of the god. On the morning of the fourth day they led him down to the cave under the temple. Now the Pythoness appeared from out of the darkness, ghostly in her long white robe. Seating herself on her throne, which was set over a cleft in the rocky floor of the cave, she began breathing in the vapours that rose from deep in the earth. Suddenly she stiffened, her eyes rolled up until only the whites showed, and when she spoke it was with the voice of Apollo.

"You have committed a great crime," said the Pythoness. "It weighs heavily on you, and you wish to be purged of your guilt."

"That is so," said Hercules. "What, then, must I do?"

"You must go to the man you dislike most in the world and perform twelve labours that he will set for you."

Hercules started, then frowned. "And who is that?" he asked, pretending he did not know. "Who is this man I so dislike?"

"No one knows that better than you do yourself," said the Pythoness.

Now shortly before this, Hercules' kinsman, Eurystheus, had become High King of Mycenae. And even though Hercules did not know that he himself would have been king had it not been for the trickery of Hera, he bitterly resented the fact that Eurystheus, who had been born on the same day he was, should rule the House of Perseus and the most powerful kingdom in Greece.

"I know of whom you speak," he growled. "And I shall never do it."

"What is your will against that of the gods?" asked the Pythoness. "When the burden of your guilt becomes heavy enough you will do it."

"Never!" said Hercules. And climbing up out of the cave he left Delphi. However, knowing that he was still defiled, he did not return to Thebes but again wandered the woods and wild places as he had before Iphicles found him.

For several weeks he lived thus, completely alone. Finally, realizing that as long as he refused to bow to the will of the gods he would not be able to marry Megara, he put aside his pride and set out for Mycenae.

4

THE FIRST
LABOUR: THE
NEMEAN LION

Copreus, herald of King Eurystheus, hurried into the great hall of the palace at Mycenae and nodded to the king.

"He is coming," he said.

Eurystheus sat up straighter on his throne, pulling his cloak around him. Hard on the herald's heels Hercules strode into the hall, and the two men looked at one another: Hercules, taller by a head than any other in the hall, his hair a reddish gold, with mighty muscles rippling under the sunburned skin of his powerful arms and an olivewood club over his shoulder; and Eurystheus, pale, with a short black beard and dark eyes, and little that was royal about him except his rich dress.

Though they had never met before, each had strong feelings about the other. Hercules disliked Eurystheus, but Eurystheus hated Hercules with a deep and abiding hatred—hated him because he knew that it was merely through an accident of birth that he was king, while Hercules had become a hero through his own strength and courage. And now, seeing Hercules for the first time, Eurystheus also feared him, and his fear increased his hatred. But he was wily, whereas Hercules was open and direct, and so he hid his feelings behind a smile, saying, "Greetings, Hercules. I have been expecting you."

"Why?" asked Hercules.

"There have been rumours for some time that you would be coming to see me."

"Bad news travels fast," said Hercules.

"I did not consider it bad news that I would soon be meeting one of my kinsmen, especially one who is so great a hero."

"It may not have been bad news for you, but it was for me," said Hercules bluntly. "I have been told that there were a few small things you might want me to do for you."

"Very small," said Eurystheus. "So small, in fact, that I am embarrassed even to mention them."

"Well, the sooner I begin, the sooner I will be finished. What's the first?"

"I thought we might begin with something truly simple," said Eurystheus. "Your first task will be to kill and flay the Nemean lion."

"It appears I have misjudged you," said Hercules. "I feared you might be making game of me and would ask me to do something really difficult." And raising his club in a salute, he left the great hall.

Though Hercules spoke lightly, he knew that this first labour of his would not be as easy as he pretended. For the Nemean lion was not only an enormous beast, far larger and even more savage and destructive than the lion he had killed near Thebes, but its skin was said to be proof against all weapons.

Arming himself, Hercules set off for Nemea, which lay north and west of Mycenae. He arrived at dusk and found the whole countryside deserted, for the lion had either killed or driven off most of those who lived there. Finally he came upon a shepherd with a tear-stained face who was about to sacrifice a ram. When Hercules asked him why he had been weeping, the shepherd said that his son had been killed by the

lion the day before. He was about to sacrifice the ram to Hera in the hope that she would keep the beast away from him and what remained of his flock.

"It may be that I shall be able to do that," said Hercules, "and also to avenge your son's death. For I am here to find and kill the lion. Give me a week's time. If I return safely, you and I will sacrifice the ram together—not to Hera, but to Zeus—for he will have aided me in this task. If I do not return, sacrifice the ram to my memory."

The shepherd agreed, and Hercules spent the night with him, in the morning setting off into the hills. For five days he searched for the lion. On the morning of the sixth day he came upon a bloody trail. He followed it to a cave high upon a lonely mountain. As he approached, the lion came out of the cave, yawned, and stretched himself. Raising his bow, Hercules sent an arrow whistling straight toward the lion's heart. The arrow shattered on its impenetrable hide.

Advancing on the beast, Hercules slashed at it with his sword. The blade broke. Dropping the useless hilt, he dealt the lion a great blow with his club. The tough olivewood splintered as if it had struck the hardest of rock. With a roar, the lion sprang at him, its jaws wide. Hercules dodged its sharp claws and closed with the lion, taking it by the throat. He now knew that what had been said about the beast was true. Its hide was indeed proof against all weapons, and his only defence lay in his own strength. Though the beast snarled savagely, trying to reach him with tooth and claw, he held it in an iron grip and his fingers tightened until he had strangled it even as he had strangled the serpents Hera had sent to destroy him when he was an infant.

Shouldering the huge carcass, Hercules started down the mountain. He reached the shepherd's hut the next evening. The shepherd was again preparing to sacrifice the ram, this time to Hercules' memory. He was overjoyed to see Hercules, and they performed the sacrifice together in thanks to Zeus.

The next day, with the lion on his shoulders, Hercules set off for Mycenae. Word of his coming had preceded him, and when he arrived, Eurystheus, surrounded by an armed guard, was waiting for him outside the city gates.

"Here is your lion," said Hercules, dropping it at Eurystheus' feet. "What next?"

Eurystheus shrank back from the monstrous beast, which, even dead, was terrifying.

"I am afraid you are not quite finished with this labour," the king told Hercules. "I said kill and *flay* it."

Hercules looked long and hard at the king. Then,

reaching for the nearest guard, Hercules took the man's sword, and turning the huge carcass on its back, he tried to skin it. But the sword's keen edge glanced off the beast's hide, and when he bore down harder on it, the blade bent as if it were made of lead. Throwing it away, Hercules growled deep in his throat like the lion itself.

Eurystheus drew back even farther.

"I will leave you to your task," he said. "When you have completed it, I will have another one for you." And hurrying into the city, he ordered the gates to be closed.

Hercules continued to stand there, looking down at the beast he had slain that still defied him. Zeus, seeing his difficulty, sent the goddess Athene to him in the shape of an old crone. Approaching him and laughing derisively, she said, "Twelve labours, Hercules, and you cannot accomplish the first?"

"Mock me not, old woman," said Hercules, "for I am not a patient man."

"And clearly stronger than you are wise." Then, "The claws, Hercules," she whispered. "The beast's own claws!"

For a moment Hercules stared at her. Then, taking hold of one of the lion's paws, he used its own razor-sharp claws to cut through the impenetrable hide.

When he had finished flaying it, he hurled the bloody carcass at the closed gates, shouting to Eurystheus, who was now watching from the top of the wall, "This is for you, Eurystheus! The skin I shall keep."

And from that day forward he dressed himself in the lion's pelt, wearing it with the gaping jaws on his head like a helmet. And with it around him he had no need for shield or breastplate, for, as he had proved himself, the dead beast's skin turned weapons more easily than the hardest bronze or iron.

5

THE
SECOND LABOUR:
THE LERNEAN
HYDRA

Though it would be a long while before he was completely purged of his guilt, now that he had bowed to the will of the gods and begun his labours Hercules felt he could go back to Thebes to visit his parents and see Megara.

From the way Megara's eyes shone when he appeared in the great hall it was clear that she had missed him as much as he had missed her.

"No, I missed you far *more* than you could possibly have missed me," she told him when they sat together in one of the walled gardens. "For while you have your labours to perform, there is little I can do to make the time pass except to think of you. And when I do, I find myself not happy, but afraid. For Eurystheus is an ingenious and a malicious man, and he has already shown that the tasks he will set for you will be not merely difficult, but dangerous."

"Still I will complete them," said Hercules. "For there is nothing I cannot accomplish for your sake. So do not think of my labours but think instead of the time when they will be finished and we can be together for good."

He spent several days in Thebes, and when he returned to Mycenae his brother, Iphicles, went with him, driving him in a chariot.

The palace watch had announced their coming to Eurystheus, and when they reached Mycenae they found the city gates closed and the king waiting for them on top of the wall. He was surrounded by guards, and his herald, Copreus, was at his side. Such was Eurystheus' fear of Hercules that from then on he was not permitted within the city or near the king. He received his instructions in this way, at a distance, and usually through Copreus.

"Well, Eurystheus," called Hercules, "what's my next task?"

Copreus conferred with Eurystheus, then said, "Who is that in the chariot with you?"

"My brother, Iphicles."

"You understand," said Copreus, "that he is not to help you. You must perform your labours all by yourself."

"Of course I understand that," said Hercules testily. "But since I am anxious to get them over with as quickly as possible, he will drive me to wherever I must go."

"Very well," said Copreus, speaking for the High King. "Then let him drive you to Lerna. When you get there, you are to kill the Hydra."

Whistling softly under his breath, Iphicles turned the chariot and started south. He had reason to look grave, for the Hydra was the most fearsome monster not only of Greece, but of anywhere in the known world. It had a huge, scaly body and nine snakelike heads, one of which was immortal. It was so venomous that its very breath could kill. Many said that it had been created especially by Hera to destroy Hercules. Whether this was true or not, the monster had appeared some years before in the Lernean swamp near the sea almost due south of Mycenae. Like the Nemean lion, it had terrorized and laid waste the entire district for miles around.

Again Zeus had told Athene, the goddess of wisdom, to help Hercules. As the hero and his brother

drove south, she thought about how he might deal
with the Hydra.

Iphicles reined in the horses at the edge of the
swamp, which stretched as far as the eye could see,
covered with reeds and dotted with pools of green,
evil-smelling water.

"Eurystheus has done well this time," said Hercules
wryly. "He has set me a task that might give pause
even to a god. To begin with, how shall I find the
Hydra?"

"I think," said Iphicles, prompted by Athene, "that
your best friend here could well be fire."

"What do you mean?" asked Hercules.

"There has been a long drought in these parts," said Iphicles. "The reeds are dry and the wind is blowing this way."

"I take your meaning," said Hercules. "Your counsel has helped me before. I shall follow it."

There was a dead tree nearby. Cutting it down, Hercules built a fire. Then he soaked some strips of cloth in oil, wrapped the cloths around the tips of several arrows, lit them, and shot the flaming arrows to the far side of the marsh. The reeds took fire and the wind blew the blaze toward the brothers. Aroused by the

roaring and crackling of the burning reeds, the Hydra rose from its lair in the centre of the swamp and came writhing toward them, all nine heads hissing.

"Remember that its breath is poisonous," said Iphicles as Hercules drew his sword. "Hold your own breath when you close with it."

Taking a deep breath, Hercules nodded. Then the monster was upon him. One of the snakelike heads darted out at him; swinging his sword, Hercules cut it off. But immediately two new heads grew from the bloody neck. Hercules cut them off also—but again new heads grew in their place, and instead of two there were four.

"Many have argued," said Hercules, falling back for a moment, "whether the Hydra had nine heads or more. I fear that before I am finished it will have nine hundred."

As he prepared to attack the hissing, many-headed monster again, Iphicles plucked a burning brand from the fire and handed it to him.

"Here," he said. "You must sear the stump each time you cut off a head as a surgeon sears a wound."

Again the Hydra writhed toward Hercules, and again Hercules cut off a head. But this time, as Iphicles had suggested, he seared the bloody stump with the blazing brand and no new heads grew in its place. In

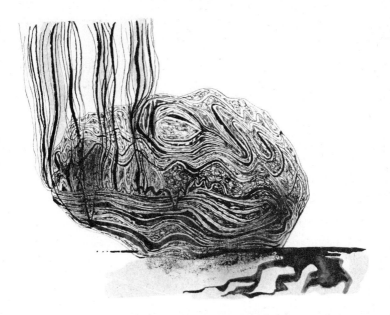

this way he cut off all its heads until only one, its immortal head, remained. With a final blow he cut that off also. But—even without a body—the head continued to hiss and blow its baleful breath toward him until he dropped a huge rock upon it, sinking it into the soft mud of the marsh.

"Again your counsel has helped me greatly," said Hercules, "even more than weapons could have. How is it that you have suddenly become as wise as you are steadfast?"

"I never counted myself wise," said Iphicles, "and I had no knowledge of what I was going to say before

I said it. It may be that one of the gods spoke with my tongue."

"That could well be," said Hercules. "And if that is so, then the greatest of them all has again proved himself my friend."

Cutting open the body of the Hydra, Hercules dipped his arrows in its gall. And this was so poisonous, that from then on the least scratch from one of them was fatal.

Eurystheus had been summoned again by the watch when Hercules and Iphicles returned to Mycenae. He was waiting on the wall above the city gate when they arrived.

"Well, Hercules," he said, "since you are still alive, I take it that you dared not attempt this labour."

"Not so, Eurystheus," said Hercules. "The Hydra is dead—except for one head, which hisses under a rock near the edge of the swamp. If you doubt me, send someone to dig it up and bring it to you."

"And you accomplished this alone, without any help from your brother?"

"He helped me this much," said Hercules. "He told me how to fight the monster and handed me burning brands to sear the wounds I made."

"Then I cannot count this as one of your labours," said Eurystheus.

Hercules looked at Eurystheus, and it was so fierce a look that even though he was high above Hercules on the city wall, the king shrank back.

"Listen to me, Eurystheus," said Hercules. "And listen well. Though it is you who sets my labours for me, I perform them not for you, but for the gods. And so I care not whether you count them, but only whether they do."

Hearing the anger in Hercules' voice, Iphicles cracked his whip and sent the horses galloping away from Mycenae and back toward Thebes. There Hercules remained until his rage had cooled sufficiently for him to perform his next task.

6

THE THIRD
LABOUR: THE
CERYNEIAN
HIND

"The High King is interested to see," said Copreus
when Hercules next appeared at Mycenae, "that this
time you have come without your brother."

"Since the High King seemed to object to his com-
ing with me even as a companion, I came alone," said
Hercules. Then, making little effort to hide his dislike:
"And what is the High King's pleasure now?"

Eurystheus, standing high above Hercules on the
city walls, whispered in Copreus' ear.

"This labour," said Copreus, "will be different from
the others in that there will be no killing in it. You
are to capture the Ceryneian hind and bring her alive
here to Mycenae."

Hercules frowned. Everyone in Greece had heard of the Ceryneian hind that lived in the wilds of Achaia, near the Gulf of Corinth. She had brass hoofs and, though a hind, had golden antlers like a stag. She was said to be the swiftest creature in the world, able to outrun even an arrow in its flight. More important, she was sacred to Artemis, the virgin goddess who was the Mistress of Wild Things.

"I do not think Artemis will like that," said Hercules.

"Nevertheless, that is your task," said Copreus.

"Very well," said Hercules with a shrug. He put down his club, bow, and sword in front of the gate. "I will not need these. Guard them for me until I return."

Tightening the thongs of his sandals, for he had a feeling that he would be travelling far, he went north and west toward Ceryneia.

It took him several days to reach it and several more to find the track of the hind. But one morning he came upon her, grazing in a forest glade. She stood at gaze for a moment, large-eyed and dappled, her golden horns gleaming in the sun. Then, wary but unafraid—for who could match her fleetness?—she bounded off through the woods, going north toward the Gulf of Corinth with Hercules running after her.

She paused again at the blue waters of the gulf.

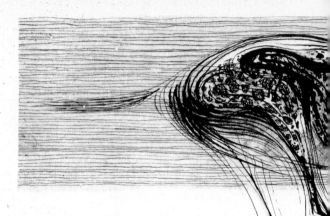

When Hercules appeared in the distance, she turned and—still unafraid—ran east toward the Isthmus.

Now began a long chase, so long and arduous that only one of more than human strength and endurance could have accomplished it. Crossing the Isthmus, the hind went north again, passing near Thespiae, where Hercules had slain his first lion, then on through Aetolia and Epirus, where, in the grove at Dodona, Zeus had one of his oldest shrines. And always Hercules came behind, never able to match the creature's speed, yet following her doggedly.

It was spring now, and, still fresh and unwearied,

the hind continued on: through Illyria, which lies alongside the Adriatic Sea, then north through the vast grasslands where the nomads roamed in their carts that were covered with bullock hides, then turning west again into the land of the Hyperboreans, the men who live at the back of the North Wind.

Summer was over now; the days were getting shorter and the weather colder. But guided by Zeus, Hercules still followed the hind. Rising at dawn, he would climb to some high point and wait till he saw the sun gleaming on her golden antlers. Then, doggedly, he would set off again on her track.

Now, anxious for the first time, the hind turned south again, thinking to find safety in the groves of Artemis. And so they retraced their steps, the hind leading and Hercules following, ever southward: back through the grasslands and along the high cliffs of Illyria, past the shrine of Zeus in Epirus and the oracle of Apollo at Delphi, through Boeotia and back across the Isthmus. And finally, a full year after the chase had begun, the hind fell exhausted on the bank of a river in the heart of Arcadia.

Slowly and quietly Hercules came up to her. Stroking her soothingly, he picked her up and slung her across his shoulders.

"Hold, Hercules," said a clear and commanding voice, and the bushes parted and the goddess Artemis herself appeared before him. Slim and beautiful, clad in skins and with her bow over her shoulder, she frowned angrily at him.

"Surely you know what beast this is," she said. "How dare you touch her?"

"Indeed I know who she is, O Artemis," said Hercules. "For I have hunted her for a full year—not through choice, but by order of Eurystheus."

"And do his commandments mean more to you than mine?"

"By no means, O goddess. Though he is the High

King and ruler of the House of Perseus, I scorn him. But in performing the labours he has set for me I am obeying the commandment of your brother Apollo, given to me by his oracle at Delphi. And he, I have always believed, spoke for all the gods. If you are angry, be not angry at me but at Eurystheus. I warned him that you would not like this."

"I do not like it," she said, "nor him. I have never liked him, and now I like him less than ever. But what will you do with my poor hind now that you have caught her?"

"I was told I must bring her alive to Mycenae. Once I have shown her to Eurystheus, I will set her free and she can return here. I give you my word that no harm will come to her."

She studied him for a moment, then nodded. "In that case, you have my leave to take her."

"Thank you, Artemis," said Hercules, and with the hind on his shoulders he set off for Mycenae.

It was almost dusk when Hercules reached the city gates and saw the High King standing on the wall waiting for him.

"Here is the Ceryneian hind, Eurystheus," he said. "What shall I do with her?"

"I will send men down to take her from you," said Eurystheus.

"You intend to keep her?"

"Of course," said Eurystheus. "I will put her in the enclosed court of my palace with my other captive beasts."

"I think Artemis will like that even less than my pursuing her."

"Nevertheless, that is my will."

The hind still on his shoulders, Hercules looked up at the king. Then he grinned. "As you say, Eurystheus. But first, I want my weapons back. And second, I will give her only to you."

Eurystheus hesitated. "Very well," he said finally.

Accompanied by Copreus and his armed guard, he went down from the wall, had the city gates opened, and came out to where Hercules waited. The captain of his guard went before him, carrying Hercules' club, bow, and sword. He put them down beside the hero, then went back to wait with his men.

"Come and get the hind, Eurystheus," said Hercules. And lifting her from his shoulders, he set her on her feet, stroking her gently and whispering to her.

Slowly and somewhat anxiously, Eurystheus came toward them. But as he reached out for the hind, Hercules released her. Like an arrow from Hercules' own bow she fled, brass hoofs spurning the earth, golden antlers flashing in the sun. In an instant she was out of sight.

As Eurystheus gazed after her, mocking laughter was heard—the laughter of the goddess.

"I am afraid you forgot how quick she was," said Hercules, shaking his head in pretended distress. "Too bad." He picked up his weapons. "It was a long, hard chase she led me. When I am rested from it I will come back and you can tell me what my next task is to be." And raising his club in salute, he set off for Thebes.

7

THE FOURTH LABOUR: THE ERYMANTHIAN BOAR

"The High King is surprised," said Copreus when Hercules again stood before the gates of Mycenae, "that it took you so long to recover from your last labour."

"It was a long chase," said Hercules, "and a lonely one. But the delay has given the High King that much more time to decide on my next task. What is it to be?"

"Because your last labour was rather difficult, the king has decided to give you one that almost anyone could accomplish. You are to capture and bring back alive the Erymanthian boar."

"I appreciate the High King's thoughtfulness," said Hercules dryly, "and I will try to complete this task more quickly than the last one." And bowing to Eurystheus, who stood beside his herald on the city walls, he set out, going west into Arcadia.

Like the hind, the Erymanthian boar was a famous beast. And like the Nemean lion and the Hydra, it was a dangerous and destructive one—larger and fiercer than any other boar in Greece. It lived on Mount Erymanthus, which was sacred to Artemis, and had for some years ravaged the countryside nearby, rooting up crops with its huge, curved tusks and killing all those who had tried to deal with it.

When Hercules reached Pholoe, he had a blacksmith make him a long, strong chain, testing each link himself for any hidden weakness. When he was satisfied with it, he paid the smith well for his work.

"Which way do you go?" asked the smith as Hercules shouldered the chain.

"North," said Hercules.

"I would not if I were you," said the smith. And he told him that a bandit named Saurus kept watch on the road, not only robbing all who came that way, but forcing them to wrestle with him and killing them.

"Thank you for your warning," said Hercules. "But since it is the shortest way to where I am going, I am afraid that I must take it." And leaving the smith shaking his head sadly—for he had liked this tall young stranger—he set off along the narrow track that led up into the hills.

At about noon, when he was high up in the hills, a hulking, black-bearded man stepped out from behind a rock, blocking his path.

"You are either very brave or very foolish to have come this way," he said. "Surely you must have heard that any who do must wrestle with me."

Hercules looked at him and at the band of ruffians who had appeared also and now stood behind him.

"If you are Saurus, I did hear that," he said mildly. "But since I am on an urgent mission, I thought I would chance it."

"Your mission will have to wait," said Saurus. "In fact, I fear it will never be completed."

"That, of course, is for the gods to decide," said Hercules. "But since you are many and I am only one, I suppose I must do as you wish." And putting down his weapons and the chain: "How many falls must we wrestle?"

"One is usually enough," said Saurus. "But I must tell you that I like to have something to show for my wrestling. I have nine and ninety skulls outside my cave, the skulls of those who have come this way before you. Yours will be the hundredth."

"And there is so much I still hoped to accomplish,"

said Hercules with a sigh. "Ah, well. Let us get it over with."

He stepped forward, hands raised in a defensive position, and Saurus rushed at him, hooking a leg behind him and trying to trip and throw him. But he might as well have tried to uproot a sturdy oak. Hold after hold he tried, but Hercules broke each one until, mad with rage, Saurus clawed at his eyes, thinking to blind him. With a roar Hercules went over to the attack. Seizing Saurus, he lifted him high over his head and dashed him to the ground with such force that every bone in his body was shattered.

For a moment Saurus' men looked down at the body of their dead chieftain. Then, with angry shouts, they came at Hercules with raised weapons. Taking up his club, Hercules fought back with such deadly effect that within a few moments more than half the bandits lay dead beside Saurus and the rest fled.

Shouldering the chain again, Hercules continued on and the next day reached Mount Erymanthus, where he began his hunt for the boar. He found its track with little trouble, and as he started to follow it the goddess Artemis again appeared before him.

"Greetings, Hercules," she said. "Why do you come here this time?"

"I hunt the Erymanthian boar," he said.

"That should not be too difficult," she replied. "I hear that your arrows are almost as deadly as mine."

"Killing it would not be difficult," he agreed. "But by Eurystheus' orders I must capture it and bring it alive to Mycenae."

"That is not quite so easy," said Artemis. "But you kept your word about my hind so I will help you."

Together they followed the boar's trail, finally coming upon the beast in a dense thicket. Seeing Hercules, the boar—large as an ox and with long, gleaming tusks—charged at him. Swinging his club deftly, Hercules struck the boar on the snout. With a squeal of pain and fear the huge beast turned and fled. Guided by Artemis, Hercules drove the boar up the mountain, the top of which was covered with snow. As the boar floundered in a deep snowdrift, Hercules leaped upon its back and bound it with his chain. Then, thanking Artemis for her help, he slung the beast over his shoulders and carried it back to Mycenae.

"Here is your boar, Eurystheus," he called to the king, dropping it before the city gates. "What you do with it is your affair. As to my next labour, that will have to wait for a while." And he set off for Pagasae in Thessaly, for he had heard that the Argonauts were gathering there for the expedition in search of the Golden Fleece and he wished to join them.

8

THE FIFTH
LABOUR: THE
AUGEAN
STABLES

"Well?" said Eurystheus as his herald came into the great hall.

"The news you received is true," said Copreus. "Hercules has returned to Greece. He is now at Thebes and should be coming here in the next day or so to continue his labours."

"Continue to win glory for himself, you mean," said Eurystheus bitterly. "So far I have given him four tasks that should have been impossible. And he has not only accomplished them, but, in doing so, has become more famous and admired than ever."

"That is because you have given him tasks that required strength and courage," said Copreus. "What if you gave him one of a different sort?"

"What sort?"

"One that would not only be difficult and unpleasant, but would make him ridiculous. For instance, my brother has just come from the west. He tells me that though he did not pass within miles of Elis, the stench from King Augeias' stables is now so great that even at a distance it made him ill. What if Hercules' next task was to cleanse the stables in one day?"

For a moment Eurystheus looked at Copreus. Then, slipping a gold ring from his finger, he gave it to him. "You are a jewel among heralds. Take this as a token of my love." And chuckling gleefully: "Hercules carrying baskets of dung on his shoulders—that will be a sight to see! Let me know when he arrives here."

Late the next afternoon Hercules arrived at Mycenae. As before, he found the Lion Gate closed and Eurystheus and his herald standing on the wall above it.

"Greetings, Hercules," said Copreus. "The High King wishes to know if you had a successful voyage."

"Very successful," said Hercules. "We brought back the Golden Fleece and also Medea, daughter of the King of Colchis. Now I am ready to continue my labours."

"The High King has thought long about it," said

Copreus. "And your next task will again be different from the last in that there will be no danger in it. In fact, it will require nothing but strength, patience—and perhaps a strong stomach."

"Somehow I do not like the sound of it," said Hercules. "What am I to do?"

"You are to clean the stables of King Augeias in one day."

"What?" roared Hercules. "Do you take me for a stableboy, a sweep, a handler of filth?"

"Nevertheless, that is your next labour," said Copreus, and fearing the wrath of Hercules even at a distance, he followed his master, who was already hurrying from the wall.

Hercules had reason to be furious, not only at the unpleasantness of the task that had been set for him, but at its enormity. For Augeias, King of Elis, had more cattle and sheep than any other man in Greece. He had been blessed by the gods in that his cows and ewes all brought forth many young, none of which ever became ill and died. But it was a mixed blessing, because several years ago his herds had become so large that it became impossible to clear away their droppings. And now the stables, cattleyard, and fields were so deep in filth that it was beginning to breed a pestilence that affected the whole region of Elis.

As Hercules raged outside the gate at Mycenae, his father, Zeus, came to his aid as he had before, again sending the goddess Athene to him in the shape of an old crone.

"Why this temper, Hercules?" she asked. "Has the High King given you a task that is too much for you?"

"Too much for anyone!" he said. "It is to clean the stables of King Augeias in one day!"

"That does sound difficult and rather unpleasant. But it is not impossible."

"How, then, shall I do it?" he asked more quietly, for he now knew that he was speaking to one of the Immortals.

"Fire was your friend when you killed the Lernean Hydra. This time your best friend would be water." And she told him what he should do.

Smiling broadly, he thanked her and set off west for Elis. Luckily, when he arrived the wind was at his back and he was able to approach to within a short distance of the royal cattleyard without being sickened by the stench. There, on the crest of a hill, he found King Augeias himself, brooding over the trick the gods had played on him in turning his good fortune into a disaster.

"Why so gloomy, O king?" asked Hercules. "You do not have the look of a man on whom the gods have smiled."

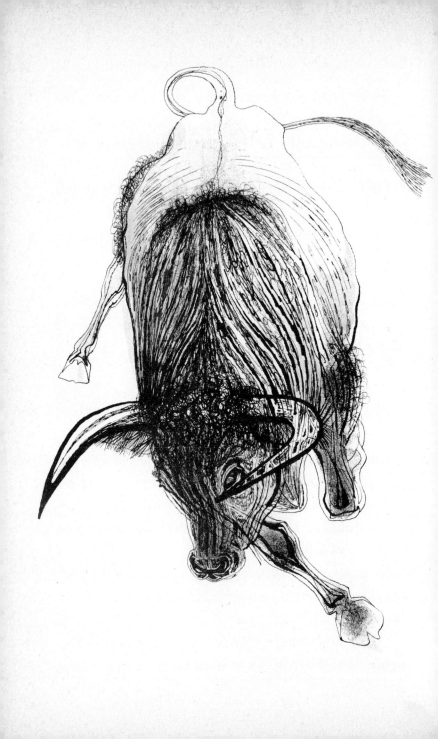

"If the wind changed or you went closer to my stables you would know why I look this way," said Augeias.

"They could stand a good cleaning," said Hercules. "If I did it for you—and did it in one day—would you give me a tenth of all your cattle?"

"Are you mocking me?" asked Augeias. "No one could do it in a day or even in a hundred days! Who are you that you even suggest such a thing?"

At that moment the largest of Augeias' bulls saw Hercules. Since he was wearing his lion skin, the bull took him for a lion and charged at him. Meeting the charge head-on, Hercules caught the bull by the horns and wrestled him to the ground.

"There is only one man in Greece who could have done that," said Augeias. "You must be Hercules."

"I am," said Hercules, releasing the bull and letting him run off—which he was glad to do

"Well, well," said Augeias. "That puts the matter in a different light. You are proposing to clean my stables in a single day?"

"In a single day and by myself."

"Then I agree," said Augeias. "If you can do it, I will give you a tenth of all my cattle."

He called up his oldest son to be a witness to their bargain, and they watched as Hercules set about his task. Picking his way carefully across the field, Hercules went to the wall that surrounded the stableyard and pulled it down in two places. Then, as Athene had suggested, he went to the nearby River Alpheus, which was swollen with spring rain. Uprooting a huge tree that grew beside the river, Hercules dropped it across the stream so that it formed a dam. The river rose quickly behind the tree trunk, overflowed its banks, and poured across the fields, through one gap in the stableyard wall and out the other, washing the yard and all the pasture about it clean. In this way, without dirtying so much as a finger, Hercules not only accomplished his labour but once again made the Kingdom of Elis a place in which men could live without fear of pestilence.

Though King Augeias should have been as grateful for this as were his subjects, when he learned that Hercules had cleansed his stables as one of the tasks set for him by Eurystheus, he refused to give him the promised cattle. And so Hercules gained nothing from this labour but greater fame.

9

THE SIXTH
LABOUR: THE
STYMPHALIAN
BIRDS

"Those who come from the west," said Copreus, "say that they can now pass quite close to Elis. The High King trusts that King Augeias appreciated what you did for him."

"I did not do it for him," said Hercules. "I did it because it was a task set for me by your master."

"Still it was a great service to Augeias," said the herald. Then, slyly: "It is too bad you couldn't collect the cattle he promised you."

"If the High King is so concerned about that, why doesn't he reward me himself?" asked Hercules. For he knew that it was Eurystheus who had told Augeias not to give him the cattle. When Copreus did not answer, he said, "Let us get on with our affairs. What is my next task to be?"

"Show him," said Eurystheus, and the herald threw the body of a huge bird down from the wall so that it fell at Hercules' feet.

"Do you know what this is?" asked Copreus.

Hercules studied the bird. It was as large as a crane, with a crane's stiltlike legs and a long, straight beak. However, its beak, claws, and feathers were all made of brass, and even in death it looked menacing.

"I have not seen one before," said Hercules, "but I suspect that it is one of the Stymphalian birds."

"It is," said Copreus. "It attacked a traveller as he passed by the marsh where they live, and he was lucky enough to be able to kill it. Your next labour will be to drive them away."

Though Hercules nodded, he knew this would not be a simple task. The birds had appeared in the marsh near Stymphalus many years before. Since then they had increased in both number and ferocity until they were a threat to all who lived in that part of Greece. For they were eaters of meat rather than of fish, and they liked the flesh of man as well as they did that of animals. Taking to the air in great flocks, they would kill both men and beasts with their strong beaks of brass, and then devour them.

Putting a new string on his bow and collecting several score more arrows, Hercules set off for Stymphalus, which lay less than half a day's journey west of Mycenae. A dense wood surrounded the marsh, and when he came out of the wood and the birds saw him, several dozen of them rose in the air, circling and diving down to attack him. Shooting with his usual speed and skill, Hercules killed as many as he could until the others flew off and joined the rest of the huge flock in the centre of the marsh.

Now again Athene appeared beside him in her guise of an old crone.

"Well shot," she said. "But there are a hundred times as many birds left as you have killed. How will you deal with them?"

"I do not know," said Hercules. For the birds were now beyond the range of even his powerful bow, and the marsh was too soft for a man to be able to walk on it.

"Perhaps these will help you," said Athene, taking a pair of brass cymbals from under her cloak.

"What shall I do with them?" asked Hercules.

"What does one usually do with cymbals?" asked Athene.

"Strike them together," said Hercules. And he did

so, making such a loud, clashing sound that he was almost deafened himself. Immediately the whole flock of birds rose from the marsh and began circling overhead. They were frightened not merely by the noise, but also by what it did to them. For since their beaks, feathers, and legs were also made of brass, the clanging of the cymbals shook them to their vitals as a struck wine goblet will make other goblets sound in sympathy.

Dropping the cymbals, Hercules picked up his bow and began shooting the birds. However, when the noise stopped, the flock settled again on the marsh, and there were nearly as many as there had been before. Again Hercules took up the cymbals and clashed them together, but this time he did not stop when the birds rose into the air. He continued until the marsh echoed with the noise, which was like the bellowing of a hundred bulls. A moment longer the birds circled overhead; then, terrified, they flew off toward the east and were never seen in Greece again.

10

THE SEVENTH LABOUR: THE CRETAN BULL

After driving off the Stymphalian birds, Hercules went again to Thebes to see his parents, his brother, and, most of all, Megara.

"Why do you sigh?" he asked her as they sat together in a quiet corner of the great hall.

"Why should I not?" said Megara. "Though you have completed half your labours, half still remain to be accomplished. And I have told you that I not only miss you but fear for you."

"And I have told you that there is naught to fear," said Hercules. "For no man ever had a greater prize waiting for him than I have in you."

She smiled at this and leaned close to him, and that smile, patient and loving, remained with him when he left Thebes and went again to Mycenae to learn what his next task was to be.

"Your last labours," said Copreus, looking down at him from the city walls, "were all close to home. For your next one the High King fears you must travel."

"Where?" asked Hercules.

"To the island of Crete," said the herald. "You must capture and bring back the Cretan bull."

Hercules groaned under his breath, not because of the difficulty of the task, but because of the time he would have to spend in journeying to complete it. However, unwilling to let Eurystheus see his dismay, he said to Copreus, "I have never been to Crete. Thank your noble master for giving me a reason for going there." And he set off for the coast, where he found a ship preparing for a voyage to Crete.

It sailed south across the dark-blue sea, landing at a port near the great city of Cnossus. Such was Hercules' fame that when King Minos heard of his arrival in Crete, he came himself to greet him and ask him what he did there.

"I do not think my mission will displease you, O king," said Hercules. "I have come to capture your bull and take it back to Greece with me."

The king looked at him thoughtfully. When Minos had come to the throne he had vowed that each year he would sacrifice the best bull in his herds to Poseidon. But one year the bull had been so big and so beautiful that Minos had decided to keep it for himself and had sacrificed the next-best bull to the sea-god. To punish him, Poseidon had turned the bull into a destroying fury. It had not only continued to grow until it was half again as big as other bulls, but it began breathing fire. And taught by Poseidon to hate man and all his works, it killed any who came near it, rooted up crops, and even attacked and levelled whole villages.

"You are right when you say I will not be displeased at your mission," said Minos. "But I do not think that even you will find it easy. For many of my bravest warriors have tried not to capture, but to kill the bull, and have themselves been killed in the attempt. However, if you can free us of this scourge, I will reward you richly."

He offered Hercules as many men as he wanted to help him, but Hercules said that all he wanted was a guide who would lead him to the bull.

The guide took him to the eastern part of the island, where they found the bull grazing near the banks of a river. When the bull saw Hercules, it lowered its head and charged at him, breathing out smoke and flame. But Hercules had armed himself with a shield of bullock's hide that was as large as he was, and now he raised this to protect himself from the bull's scorching breath. Bracing himself, he withstood the monster's charge, stopping it in its tracks. Then, dropping the shield, he seized the bull by the horns, and putting forth all his strength, threw it to the ground.

Half dazed, the bull staggered to its feet, and again Hercules threw him. The terrified bull fled to the river and started to swim across. But Hercules went after him, catching him in midstream and turning him so that he was forced to swim down the river.

In this way, with water quenching the monster's flaming breath, they came to the coast where Minos had a ship waiting for them. Hercules lashed the bull to the ship's side, and after Minos had thanked him and given him many rich gifts, they sailed back to Greece.

Exhausted by the voyage and by his long immersion in the sea, the bull was completely subdued when Hercules led him to the gates of Mycenae.

"Here is the Cretan bull, O king," said Hercules. "What would you have me do with him?"

But even though it stood there quietly for the moment, the bull was so fearsome that Eurystheus said,

"Set him free."

"I do not think the people of Greece will thank you for that," said Hercules. "But what happens will be on your head, not mine."

He released the bull, slapping it on the rump, and it lumbered off, crossing the Isthmus and wandering north through Attica to Marathon, where it again became as fierce as it had been on Crete, ravaging the whole region until it was killed some years later by Hercules' kinsman, Theseus.

11

THE EIGHTH LABOUR: THE MARES OF DIOMEDES

Angry at the ease with which Hercules had completed the labours he had given him so far, Eurystheus again consulted his herald as to what he should have him do next.

"Have you heard of the mares of King Diomedes?" asked Copreus.

"I have heard of Diomedes," said Eurystheus. "He rules the Bistonians in Thrace. But I have not heard of his mares."

"Few have heard of them," said Copreus. "For though the Bistonians are a fierce and warlike people, they speak of the mares in whispers. For they are man-killers and man-eaters, so savage that Diomedes keeps them tethered with iron chains. It is said that he feeds them on the flesh of strangers and unsuspecting guests." Copreus paused. "Would you not like to see horses such as these?"

"I would indeed," said Eurystheus, his eyes suddenly bright. "Thank you, Copreus."

And so, when Hercules appeared again before the gates of Mycenae, Copreus said, "Your next labour will be to capture and bring here to the High King the mares of Diomedes."

Hercules looked thoughtfully at the herald, for unlike Eurystheus he had heard about Diomedes' mares.

"Thrace is a long journey," he said. "Would the High King mind if I took some companions with me to keep me company?"

The herald turned to Eurystheus, who nodded. "The High King does not object," he said. "You may do so."

"Thank the High King for me," said Hercules. And saluting him, he returned to Thebes.

When he let it be known what his next labour was, all the young men of Thebes volunteered to come with him. Selecting a dozen of the bravest, among them a skilled horse-tamer named Abderus, he set sail for Thrace.

They sailed north and east through the Aegean Sea,

passing close to the island of Samothrace, which was sacred to the Triple Goddess, then turning north and landing on the coast of Thrace near the city of Tirida. The land there was low and marshy, and the Bistonians had built a dyke along the shore to keep out the sea.

Drawing their ship up on the beach, they climbed over the dyke and crossed the marshy plain beyond it to Tirida, arriving just before nightfall. The guards at the gate were astonished to see them, for all who travelled in those parts knew how dangerous it was to fall into the hands of Diomedes. But when Hercules asked for the king, they took him and his companions into the great hall of the palace.

"Hercules," said Diomedes, studying him. "It seems to me that I have heard of you. But what brings you to Thrace?"

"I have heard of you also," said Hercules. "I have also heard of your mares and would like to see them."

"What have you heard about them?" asked Diomedes.

"That they are quite unusual," said Hercules. "Different from other horses in that they do not graze or eat corn."

"That is true," said Diomedes. "They are different from any other horses anywhere in the world. And see them you shall, but not tonight. Tonight you shall feast with me and in the morning you will see my mares."

He gave orders to his steward, and a great feast was served to Hercules and his companions and all the warriors in the hall. There were many courses in the feast—fish and fowl as well as meat—and as Diomedes kept urging his guests to eat more and still more, it was clear to Hercules what was in his mind. He knew that Diomedes was thinking, "Eat well, dear guests. The better you eat tonight, the better my mares will eat tomorrow."

Throughout the feast great goblets of wine were served to all in the hall, but Hercules whispered to his comrades that they must not drink so much as a drop. The wine was strong and served unmixed with water. In addition, Hercules feared that the guests' portions might contain the juice of the poppy, which will make a man sleep so soundly that nothing awakens him. Therefore, though the visitors pretended to drink, they poured the wine out under the table. The result was that by midnight all in the great hall except Hercules and his companions were drunken and snoring.

When he was satisfied that all the Bistonians were asleep, Hercules rose, and taking a torch, led his comrades to the stables. These were easy to find, since the wall surrounding them was covered with the bones of those the mares had already eaten. Overpowering the grooms, they went inside to the separate stalls where the mares were kept.

When the mares saw the men, they reared, bared their teeth, and began pulling at the iron chains that held them in their stalls, for they had not been fed that day and were ravenously hungry. Hercules and his men used the chains as halters, binding the mares' mouths with them so that they could not bite, and led them out of the city, and back across the plain.

They had almost reached the dyke when they heard angry shouts in the distance and saw flaring torches; they realized that the grooms had freed themselves and given the alarm.

"I fear we shall have to fight," said Abderus. "And we are greatly outnumbered."

"I do not mind fighting if I have to," said Hercules. "But I do not think it will be necessary."

Going to the dyke, he tore down a portion of it. The tide was high and the sea came pouring through, flooding the plain and making a vast lake that cut off their pursuers. Feeling safe, they decided to wait until daybreak before setting sail, for the waters in those parts were shallow and dangerous and they were afraid they might run aground. Just before dawn, however, they heard the clash of arms, and there, coming up the beach toward them, was a large party of Bis-

tonians whom Diomedes had led around the lake.

"Hold, Hercules," he shouted. "You would not take my mares away without feeding them first, would you?"

"No," said Hercules. "That would be cruel. But I think they have grown tired of the flesh of strangers and would like a change."

With the help of Abderus, he took off the chains that bound the mares' mouths and drove them toward the Bistonians. When Diomedes saw them charging toward him, he turned to run, but it was too late. The mares were upon him, and thus he died. Hercules and his companions followed close behind, but they had no need to use their arms, for the mares killed many of the Bistonians and the rest fled.

Hercules allowed the mares to eat their fill. Then, when their hunger was satisfied, he bound them again with the iron chains, led them onto the ship, and sailed back to Greece, where he delivered them to Eurystheus.

Eurystheus was, of course, terrified of the mares. And though Abderus offered to tame them for him, he dedicated them to Hera and freed them on Mount Olympus, where, fierce as they were, they were finally killed by wild beasts who were even more savage than they were.

12

THE
NINTH LABOUR:
HIPPOLYTE'S
BELT

At about this time Eurystheus was arranging for the marriage of his oldest daughter. And it was because he wanted a wedding gift that would be worthy of her that he selected Hercules' next labour.

When Hercules appeared before the gates of Mycenae, Copreus, speaking for his master, said, "Your task this time should not be too difficult, noble Hercules. And since it is said that you will soon be getting married yourself, it is one that you should enjoy."

"As always," said Hercules, "the longer your introduction, the more certain I am that I will not like what follows. So get on with it. What am I to do?"

"It is the High King's wish that you bring here as a marriage gift for his daughter the golden belt of Hippolyte, Queen of the Amazons."

"No," said Hercules.

"Are you refusing to perform this labour?"

"Yes, I am. I do not mind tasks that are dangerous. But how am I to perform this one? Queen Hippolyte is not likely to give me her belt merely because I ask for it. Does the High King expect me to take it by force?"

"Why not?"

"Because I do not fight with women!"

"By all accounts, the Amazons are far fiercer warriors than any men. Are you sure you are not refusing because you are afraid?"

"I have not yet met anyone, man or woman, of whom I am afraid," said Hercules hotly.

"Well, that is your next task," said Copreus. "What will happen if you refuse it is between you and the gods." And he followed Eurystheus down from the city walls, both of them pleased that they had at last provoked Hercules.

Hercules was still furious when he returned to Thebes. He was angry not only because of the difficulty of this particular labour, but because it was another one that would require a long journey and thus further delay his marriage to Megara. However, when he had thought about it, he realized that he had no choice in the matter, so he again recruited a company of young men, took a ship, and set sail for the Black Sea, where the Amazons lived. And this time, as he had before, his brother, Iphicles, went with him.

They sailed north and east across the Aegean, through the narrow Hellespont, passing by the high stone walls of Troy, and entered the Black Sea by way of the Bosporus. Then they set their course eastward along the southern coast of the Black Sea. All this was familiar to Hercules, for he had come this way before when he went with the Argonauts to fetch the Golden Fleece. But while they had passed by the country of the Amazons on that voyage, they had not landed there, and Hercules had no idea how they would be received when they arrived nor how he would win Hippolyte's belt.

The Amazons lived on the southern shore of the Black Sea near the mouth of the river Thermodon. And though they were a nation of women, for they had driven out all their men many years before, they were as fierce and warlike as Copreus had said. They fought on horseback, shooting a short bow and wielding a battle-axe, and they were so skilled in the use of these weapons that they had conquered all the tribes who lived near them.

Hercules and his company anchored their ship at

the mouth of the Thermodon and went ashore to where Hippolyte waited with her bodyguard. She was tall, almost as tall as Hercules, and very beautiful. She wore a short tunic of leopard skin, and the famous belt, two handsbreadths wide and cunningly wrought of shining gold, was clasped about her waist. She studied Hercules, and it was clear that she approved of him.

"You are a proper man," she said. "Far more of a man than any I have ever seen before. Who are you and whence do you come?" And when Hercules had told her: "What do you want here, Hercules?"

"I have come here for your golden belt," he said.

She quieted her bodyguard, a group of heavily armed young women, who had stirred angrily at this.

"Why do you want it?" she asked.

"It is a task that was set for me by Eurystheus, High King of Mycenae," he said, and he told her of the crime he had committed in his madness and the penance that had been decreed for him by the gods.

"That is a good reason," she said. "And did you think I would give you the belt?"

"I have not thought of how I would get it," he said. "You asked me why I was here and I told you."

"You are as truthful as you appear to be strong," she said. "It would not be right for me to give it to

you, for it is not mine alone but belongs to all the
Amazons. It was given by Ares, the god of war, to
the nymph Harmonia, from whom we are all descended, and it has been worn ever since by the queen.
However, I will make a bargain with you. I will
wrestle with you, and if you defeat me, you may have
it."

Now Hippolyte had fallen in love with Hercules
as soon as she saw him, and she would have been
happy to give him the belt as a love gift. But fearing
what the Amazons might say and do, she suggested
the contest so that when she lost she could claim it
was the will of the gods.

"I cannot wrestle with a woman," said Hercules.

"Why?" she asked. "Are you afraid I will beat
you?"

This was very much what Copreus had said, and
remembering his answer, Hercules said, "No, I am not
afraid of that. I have never fought with a woman
before. But if that is the only way I can win the
golden belt, I will do so now."

"Very well," said Hippolyte. "Have your men pre-
pare the wrestling ground."

While the Greeks trampled down the sand of the
beach, packing it hard for wrestling, Hippolyte re-
tired a short distance with her bodyguard. Her warriors

surrounded her, hiding her from the view of Hercules and his companions, and there was much whispering and some laughter.

"She must know that she cannot stand against you," said Iphicles. "They are planning some kind of trick."

"I think so too," said Hercules. "We will have to see what it is."

When Hippolyte came forward for the wrestling she was not wearing the golden belt—she had taken it off and given it to the captain of her bodyguard to hold—and her bare limbs gleamed. She approached Hercules and he tried to seize her, but she slipped from his grasp with ease. When she had gone off with her warriors she had had them rub her body with bear grease, and she was now as slippery as an eel. Again and again Hercules grasped her, trying for a hold, but each time she slipped away from him. The Amazons and even the Greeks were laughing now, for it seemed a great jest to them that Hercules, for all his strength, could do nothing with her. Then suddenly Hercules changed his tactics. Instead of trying for a hold on her body he took her by her hair, twisting his fingers in it until he had a firm grip. Then, taking her by the ankles with his other hand, he lifted her easily and set her down on her back.

"Well done, Hercules," she whispered.

"Do you admit that you have been beaten?"

"I do," she said, rising to her feet again. "I will not give you the belt now, but I will tonight. You and your men must come to our camp for a feast, and afterward you shall have it."

"As you say, O queen," replied Hercules.

"Again I am not sure I trust her," said Iphicles when the Amazons had left.

"This time I do not agree with you," said Hercules. "I think she means to give me the golden belt. But in any case we shall go to the feast armed."

At dusk Hercules and his companions went to the Amazons' camp, where Hippolyte greeted them and led them to the royal tent. She seated Hercules at her right hand, and slaves served them food and wine. When they had eaten their fill Hercules said, "You have been most hospitable, Hippolyte. But it is growing late. Now may I have the belt?"

"I promised it to you and you shall have it," said Hippolyte. "But the reason I asked you to come here tonight was to tell you that, if you like, you can have more than the belt."

"What do you mean?" asked Hercules.

"While we have no men among us, it is not because we do not like men, but only that there are none in these parts who are our equals as warriors. You are certainly that, and many of those in my bodyguard look favourably on your companions. What I propose is that you stay here with us. If you will do so and marry me, you shall rule the Amazons with me and your companions shall be given high rank among us."

"I am greatly honoured by your proposal," said Hercules, "but I am afraid it is impossible. I still have three labours to perform, and in any case I could not marry you because I am betrothed to another."

"But need you return to Greece at once?" asked Hippolyte. "Can you not at least stay here with us for a while?"

Now Hera, who had always hated Hercules, had

been watching what was happening there on the shores of the Black Sea. When she saw how easily Hercules was accomplishing this labour she became angrier than ever. Taking the shape of an Amazon, she went about among the warrior-women telling them that Hercules had not come there only for the belt, but that he planned to abduct their queen and take her back to Greece with him.

Before Hercules could answer Hippolyte, her body-guard came bursting into the tent, shouting, "Fear not, Hippolyte! We will save you!"

"Save me from what?" she asked.

"From these Greek schemers," said the captain of her guard, and raising her bow, she loosed an arrow at Hercules. But as she did so, Hippolyte threw herself in front of him, taking the arrow in her own breast and falling to the ground dying.

With a roar Hercules leaped over the table, his club in his hand, and slew the Amazon who had mortally wounded the queen. His companions drew their swords and for a few moments there was a fierce battle. But though the Amazons far outnumbered the Greeks, they were no match for them, especially with a raging Hercules leading them, and they soon broke and fled.

Returning to the tent, Hercules knelt beside Hippolyte. She had unfastened her belt, and holding it out

to him she said, "Here, Hercules. When I said you could have more than my belt, I meant you could have my love. But you may have my life too." And then she died.

The next morning Hercules and his companions buried the Amazon queen, sacrificing many bulls in her honour, and then set sail for Greece. When they arrived, Hercules gave the belt to Eurystheus, but he gave it to him with a heavy heart. For he knew that Eurystheus would in turn give it to his daughter, and it did not seem right to him that anyone less brave and less noble than Hippolyte should wear it.

13

THE
TENTH LABOUR:
THE CATTLE
OF GERYON

"Whose cattle," asked Copreus when Hercules next appeared at Mycenae, "are the most famous and beautiful in the world?"

"It was my understanding that I was to perform twelve tasks that your master would set for me," said Hercules. "Nothing was said about my answering questions for him."

"The question concerns your next task," said Copreus. "Since you have travelled far more widely than most men, the High King thought you would know the answer. If you do not, I will tell you."

"Of course I know the answer," said Hercules. "You must mean the cattle of Geryon."

"You are right," said Copreus. "You accomplished your last labour very easily, since Queen Hippolyte gave you her belt when you asked for it. This time you are to get Geryon's cattle without either asking for them or paying for them and bring them back here to the High King."

Hercules grimaced unhappily. Apart from its other difficulties, this task, too, involved a long journey. But since the sooner he began the sooner he would return, he set off at once.

Geryon was the King of Tartessus in Spain. He was descended from the Titan Oceanus and had been born with three heads, six hands, and three bodies joined together at the waist. And since each of his bodies was more powerful than that of an ordinary mortal, he was said to be the strongest man in the world. His cattle were large, red, and very beautiful. They were guarded by Eurytion, a son of Ares, and by a huge watchdog.

Though Hercules could have gone to Spain by ship, he knew he would have to bring the cattle back by land, and he decided to journey there that way to search out the best route for his return. He went north to Istria and then west through the Alps and along the coast through the southern part of Gaul, slaying bandits and other evildoers he chanced to meet and mak-

ing the way safe for other travellers. He crossed the Pyrenees and went south again until he reached the mountain slopes facing Africa where the cattle grazed.

As he approached, the watchdog scented him, barked loudly, and came bounding down toward him. The dog was a shaggy creature, as large and fierce as a lion. With a growl it leaped for his throat, but swinging his club deftly, Hercules killed it with a single blow. Eurytion, Geryon's herdsman, had been resting in the shade of a rock, but the dog's barking roused him, and seeing Hercules he came running toward him also. Like Hercules he carried a huge club, and raising it high he struck a mighty blow at Hercules. Hercules dodged the blow, struck in his turn, and Eurytion fell lifeless to the ground.

Hercules began rounding up the cattle. Though larger than other cattle, the beasts were docile, and they began moving off down the mountain ahead of Hercules. But there were other herdsmen on the hills nearby. They sent word of what was happening to Geryon, and when Hercules reached the level plain below, Geryon himself appeared.

"Hold, stranger!" he shouted. "If you want my cattle you must fight for them."

Hercules turned, prepared to do battle. Geryon

strode toward him brandishing three spears, one in the right hand of each of his bodies. With sudden and surprising speed he threw all three at Hercules. But quick as Geryon was, Hercules was not taken by surprise. He threw himself down and the spears whistled over his head. Next, as Geryon drew three swords, Hercules whipped an arrow from his quiver, loosed it, then let fly a second and a third, shooting so rapidly that all three were in the air at the same time. All the arrows flew true, each striking Geryon in one of his hearts, and his shade joined that of his herdsman in the Underworld.

Now Hercules began the long journey back to Mycenae. Following the route he had taken on his way to Tartessus, he drove the cattle through a pass in the Pyrenees and then along the coast through southern Gaul. Since the cattle were so beautiful and he was alone, almost every day Hercules had to fight off those who would steal the cattle from him. But the greatest peril he faced came now as he was driving the cattle through Liguria in the north of Italy.

Word had come to the King of Liguria that a herd of magnificent cattle, larger and more beautiful than any that had ever been seen before, were being driven through his country, and he decided that he must have them. But since he was also told that it was Hercules who drove the cattle, he took with him a war party of several hundred of his bravest warriors.

When Hercules saw the king and his men marching toward him across the plain he knew why they had come, and he took up his position between them and the cattle.

"Greetings, Hercules," said the king. "From the way you frown I think you must know why we are here."

"I do, O king," said Hercules. "And I warn you that you will be no more successful than any of the others who have tried to take these cattle from me."

"I do not know about the others, but I do not think that even you will be able to stop us. And since no cattle, not even these, are worth your life, I urge you not to try."

"I fear not for my life," said Hercules, "but I fear for yours. For if you attack me Liguria will need a new king, and there are few of those who are with you who will not leave their bones here."

"You are as brave as I have heard you were," said the king. "At least you talk bravely. Now we will see how you fight and how you die." And drawing his sword, he signalled his men to advance.

Hercules had strung his bow and laid his quiver on the ground before him. As the Ligurians came toward him, he began shooting. His first arrow was aimed at the king, and though the king had raised his shield to protect himself, the arrow pierced his shield and his brass breastplate, and he fell dead where he stood. Arrow after arrow Hercules loosed, and so deadly was his aim that the Ligurians hesitated and finally drew back.

But now Hercules was in a serious plight. For all his arrows were gone, and though he still had his club he knew that if the Ligurians closed with him he could not stand for long against them. He looked about him for anything that he could use to hold them off, but the plain was sandy and there were not even stones in sight.

The king's brother now took command, and seeing that Hercules had no more arrows left, he rallied the Ligurians and ordered them to attack again.

As they formed a battle line and came toward him, determined to avenge the death of their king, Hercules raised his eyes and called on Zeus, saying, "Father Zeus, though you have shown me your favour and been my friend many times in the past, I have never asked you for help. But I do so now, for I have never needed it more. Aid me and if I live I shall sacrifice the finest of these cattle to you."

Immediately the sky darkened, thunder rumbled,

and there fell from the clouds overhead—not rain—
but a shower of stones. They fell on the Ligurians,
striking many of them dead. With a shout Hercules
ran forward, and picking up the stones began hurling
them at the Ligurians. His aim with these was as deadly
as it had been when he loosed his arrows. This shower
of stones, from above and from the hand of Hercules,
was too much for the Ligurians, and they turned and
fled, leaving most of their number lying dead on the
plain.

True to his promise, Hercules built a fire, selected
the finest bull in the herd, and sacrificed it as an offering of thanks to Zeus. After his sacrifice Hercules continued on his way. And though the road was often
difficult, and many times he had to fight off men who
would take the cattle from him, he was never again
in such danger as he had been on the plain in Liguria.
In the end he drove the cattle to the gates of Mycenae,
thus completing the tenth of his labours.

14

THE ELEVENTH LABOUR: THE APPLES OF THE HESPERIDES

It was now more than eight years since Hercules had begun his labours, and in that time his brother, Iphicles, had had several children. Megara, of course, loved these young nieces and nephews of hers and often helped her sister care for them. But on this sunny morning—the morning of the day Hercules was to leave Thebes again for Mycenae—her eyes were dark and sad as she looked at the children. For Hercules was playing with them, tossing the boys high in the air and holding the girls on his knees. Glancing at Megara, Hercules put the children by and came over to her, taking her hand in his.

"You know what is in my mind," she said.

"How should I not know when it is in my mind too?" he said. "You were wishing that these children were ours." And when she nodded: "I know how hard this has been for you, Megara. But it has been hard for me too. Be patient but a little while longer and we shall have that which we both want so much—as many children as these: tall, strong sons and daughters who will be as beautiful as you are."

"I sometimes fear that the gods are jealous of us and that your labours will never end," she said with a sigh. "But I will try to be patient." And she smiled bravely as she said farewell to him.

When Hercules arrived at Mycenae he could tell from the way Eurystheus looked at him that he felt he had finally thought of a labour that would be beyond even his powers. He greeted Hercules and then watched as his herald said, "Your next task, noble Hercules, will be to get and bring back here to the High King some of the golden apples of the Hesperides."

Hercules now knew why the king had looked at him that way. For while most of the Greeks had heard of the apples of the Hesperides—golden apples growing on a golden tree, the wedding gift of Mother Earth to the goddess Hera—no one knew where they were to be found. But still unwilling to give Eurystheus even a moment's satisfaction, Hercules hid his concern. Instead he nodded casually to the High King and set off as if this labour were no more difficult than any of the others.

He had gone but a short distance when he came on the old crone whom he now knew to be the goddess Athene.

"Greetings, Hercules," she said. "Where are you off to now?"

"I do not know," he confessed. "My task this time is to bring back some of the apples of the Hesperides."

"Ah," she said. "That would not be easy even if you knew where they were. If I were you, I would ask the sea-god Nereus about it."

"And where shall I find him?"

"At the mouth of the river Po."

Though Hercules suspected that if she wished she could herself tell him where he would find the apples, he thanked her and set off along much the same road he had taken with the cattle of Geryon.

When he reached the mouth of the river Po, the river nymphs showed Hercules where Nereus lay asleep, and creeping toward him quietly, he seized the white-haired old sea-god.

Like all sea-gods, Nereus could assume any shape

he wished. Now, though taken by surprise, he changed himself first into a lion and then into a serpent, a panther, a boar, running water, and a tall, leafy tree. But Hercules held on to him grimly through all these transformations. Finally Nereus became himself again and said with grudging admiration, "It seems that, among other things, you are stubborn and steadfast. I assume you wish to ask me something. What is it you want to know?"

"I would like you to tell me where I can find the apples of the Hesperides and how I can get them."

"I can tell you where they are," said Nereus. "They are in a walled garden on the slopes of the mountains that face the sea far to the west."

"I have been to the far west," said Hercules. "To Tartessus."

"The garden of the Hesperides is farther west than that," said Nereus. "It is across the strait that separates Spain from Africa. It is so far west that the chariot-horses of the sun end their daily journey and take a rest there until they must begin it again. But though reaching the garden will be difficult, it will be far easier than getting the apples. For they are watched by the dragon Ladon who never sleeps."

"I have dealt with the Hydra," said Hercules. "I should be able to deal with a dragon."

"Perhaps," said Nereus. "But how will you deal with the Hesperides, the daughters of the giant Atlas, who also watch the apples? Will you slay them too?"

"No, I cannot do that," said Hercules. "But there must be some way I can accomplish this labour."

"It may be that there is," said Nereus. "Atlas, who carries the heavens on his shoulders, holding earth and sky apart, is stationed on the peak of the tallest mountain nearby. His burden is a heavy one, and if you offer to take it from him he might be willing to get the apples for you."

"I thank you, Nereus," said Hercules, releasing him.

"Wait," said the sea-god. "Since I have told you so much, I will tell you one thing more. If Atlas should give you his burden, he will not be anxious to take it back again and he will probably offer to deliver the apples for you. You must not agree to this, for once he has tasted freedom it is unlikely that he will ever return."

Again Hercules thanked him and set off on his journey. He went west through Gaul and then down through Spain till he stood on the huge rock that looked across the strait toward Africa. He erected a tall column here; then, descending the rock, he plunged into the sea, swam across the strait, and erected another column on the African side. And from that time on men have called this place where the waters of the Mediterranean mingle with the ocean stream the Pillars of Hercules.

Now Hercules went west until he came to the mountain peak where the Titan Atlas stood, his shoulders bowed under the weight of the heavens.

Hercules greeted him, and said, "I am Hercules. And I am here because I thought you might help me with a task that was set for me by Eurystheus, King of Mycenae."

"What is the task?"

"I am to bring him some of the golden apples that grow in the garden of your daughters, the Hesperides."

Atlas looked at him thoughtfully. "If anyone can help you, it is I. But there are two difficulties. The first is the dragon Ladon, who guards the tree and will allow no one near it except my daughters."

"I can deal with him," said Hercules, showing Atlas his bow. "My arrows never miss."

"The second difficulty is my burden, a punishment laid on me by Zeus for joining my brothers in the revolt against him. By his commandment, it can never be put down."

"There is no difficulty about that either," said Hercules. "I will take it on my shoulders if you will get the apples for me."

A cunning look came into Atlas' eyes.

"Deal with the dragon," he said, "and then we will see."

Walking to the far side of the peak, Hercules looked down into the walled garden. The tree with its golden fruit gleamed in the centre, and coiled about the tree was the dragon. Hercules whistled shrilly, and when the dragon raised his head he loosed the arrow that he had ready on the string. It flew straight and true, and the dragon fell dead.

"Well done," said Atlas. "Now let us see if you can take this burden from me."

Standing beside him, Hercules spread his powerful legs and bent his back; slowly Atlas lowered the heavenly vault until it was resting on his shoulders. Zeus strengthened his limbs and Hercules straightened up again.

"That is well done also," said Atlas. "I did not think there was another on earth who could hold up the sky as I have been doing even for a moment." He sighed happily, stretching and flexing his mighty muscles. "Now I will fulfil my part of the bargain."

He strode down the mountain to the garden, talked to his daughters, and a short while later returned with three of the golden apples.

"You have done me a great favour," he said, "in giv-

ing me my freedom after all these centuries. To show my gratitude, I will do something for you. If you will hold up the heavens for a few months longer, I will take these apples to Eurystheus for you."

Though Hercules had been expecting this, he shifted uneasily.

"Be careful!" said Atlas anxiously as the heavens shook and a few stars fell.

"I will," said Hercules. "And if you're sure you won't be gone for longer than that, I might well consider it. But first I'd like you to take back the heavens for a moment while I make a pad of my lion skin and put in on my shoulders."

"Of course," said Atlas. And laying down the golden apples, he took the heavenly vault back from Hercules. Now it was Hercules' turn to sigh with relief and stretch.

"You said that I had done you a favour," he said. "But it is the other way round. It is you who did me one by getting me the apples. And since this is so, I would not dream of imposing on you further by letting you deliver them for me. So please accept my thanks for your great kindness." And saluting Atlas ironically, he picked up the apples and went off with them.

Hercules did not return to Mycenae the way he had come, but went east through Libya. Antaeus, King of

Libya, was the son of Poseidon and Mother Earth, and it was his custom to make all strangers wrestle with him. He was not only a huge and powerful man and a skilled wrestler, but every time he touched the earth his strength was increased so that he always won. However, he was not content with merely winning. He ended the contest not by pinning his opponent or forcing him to yield, but by killing him and adding his skull to those of his other unhappy victims on the roof of the temple of Poseidon.

He met Hercules near the cave in which he lived, sleeping on the bare ground so as to preserve and increase his already prodigious strength. He told Hercules of the custom and challenged him. Somewhat reluctantly Hercules accepted his challenge, set down his club and the golden apples, and stepped forward for the contest.

He noticed that in preparing for the wrestling, Antaeus took up handfuls of sand and rubbed them over his body, but he did not know why the king did so.

The match began, and for several minutes neither had the advantage. Finally Hercules got the hold he had been seeking, tripped Antaeus, and threw him full length to the ground. Antaeus lay there for a moment and Hercules thought it was because he had been hurt. But when he rose and they closed again, Hercules found that he was stronger than before, rather than weaker. Again they strained at one another, again Hercules finally got a grip and threw him. And again when Antaeus rose he was stronger than before.

Then, at last, Hercules remembered who the mother of his opponent was, and guessed Antaeus' secret. And knowing that, he realized that he was in sore straits. For how could he win against someone whose strength was not only restored but increased every time he touched the ground? In that dark moment, however, Hercules knew what he must do. Instead of trying to throw Antaeus again, he raised him high in the air, and holding him there, away from all contact with the earth, he strangled him.

Hercules went on through Egypt, where he founded a city that he named Thebes in honour of his birthplace, and then took a ship home to Greece.

He brought the golden apples to Mycenae and gave them to Eurystheus. But fearing Hera's wrath, Eurystheus dared not keep them and returned them to him. Hercules then took them to the temple of Athene and laid them on the altar as an offering for the help she had given him. But even Athene was unwilling to risk the anger of Hera, and now that the labour was completed, she gave the apples back to the Hesperides and they were seen among men no more.

15

THE TWELFTH LABOUR: THE CAPTURE OF CERBERUS

"Now I must go," said Hercules to Megara. "For the sooner I do, the sooner I will return." Then: "My dear, why do you cling to me so?"

"Because I am afraid," she said. "More afraid than ever."

"Do you doubt that I will come back to you?"

"I do not know what I am afraid of," she said. "But I am. I told you I feared the gods might be jealous of us."

"None of the gods would be so heartless as to keep us apart when we have waited for so long to marry," said Hercules. "I asked you to be patient before, but this is my last labour. When I have completed it, we will never be separated again." And kissing her tenderly, he started out of the courtyard.

He paused at the doorway and looked back at her, and as she had before, Megara tried hard to smile bravely at him. Somehow that smile—which could not hide her distress—touched him as deeply as the memory of her beauty and remained with him even longer. Waving to her, he set off for Mycenae for the last time.

Eurystheus, meanwhile, was conferring again with his herald Copreus.

"Since this is his twelfth labour, it should be the most difficult of all," said the High King. "But what task can I set him that will be harder for him to accomplish than what he has already done? There are few places on earth to which he has not been. And I do not think there is any place in the world to which he could not go."

"Perhaps you should be concerned," said Copreus, "not about where he goes but about whether he can come back. What if, for this labour, you sent him to a place from which no man has ever returned?"

"What place is that?" asked Eurystheus.

"Tartarus," said Copreus. "The Underworld."

Eurystheus looked at him thoughtfully. "I have already given you a ring as a token of my esteem. Take now this bracelet. The Underworld. Why not? If he can go there and return he will deserve to be called the greatest hero Greece has ever known."

And so when Hercules appeared before the Lion Gate at Mycenae, Copreus said to him, "Your last labour, Hercules, will be to bring back from Tartarus the watchdog, Cerberus."

Though Hercules had expected his final labour to be the most difficult of all, he paled at this. As Copreus had told the king, no man had been to the Underworld, the realm of Hades, and returned. And even if he arrived there and was able to come back, how would he be able to bring Cerberus with him? This watchdog who guarded the gate of Tartarus was a frightening monster. He had three heads, a mane of serpents, and a tail with a poisoned barb at the end of it like that of a scorpion. Hercules' only comfort was the knowledge that if he accomplished this task he would be free of Eurystheus and free to marry Megara. This strengthened his resolve to complete the labour, in spite of its hazards, and complete it as quickly as possible.

Before he set out for the Underworld, however, he went to Eleusis and asked to be initiated into the sacred rites that were called the Mysteries. He did this because the Eleusinians claimed to know the secrets of the Underworld, and those who were initiated into the

Mysteries were taught how to deal with the dangers they would face there.

After he had learned all that the Eleusinians could teach him, and been accepted as an initiate, Hercules journeyed to the southern part of the Peloponnese, where there was an entrance to Tartarus. Here he was met by Hermes, the messenger of the gods who was also the guide of the souls of the dead, and he led Hercules into the cleft in the earth. Down they went into the darkness, lit now by the glow of Hermes' staff, ever down until they reached the river Styx—the wide, dark, underground river that separates the living from the dead. They roused Charon, the old man who ferries souls across the Styx, and Hercules paid him his fare with a silver coin. But when Hercules stepped into the boat it sank down almost to the gunwales.

"What's this?" said Charon. "In all the centuries that I have been ferryman no shade ever weighed so much. And if you are not a shade, I cannot take you over."

"You will take me over," said Hercules, scowling at him, "or it is you who will become a shade."

Charon drew back from him, but when Hermes reassured him, he picked up his oars and ferried Hercules and his guide across the dark, slow-moving river.

A crowd of shades had gathered on the far side of

the Styx, anxious to see if the new arrival was one they knew. When they realized that Hercules was not a ghost as they were, all fled except two. One of these was Medusa, the Gorgon who had been slain by Hercules' ancestor Perseus. When Hercules saw her, with her frightening face and snake-crowned head, he raised his club, but Hermes restrained him.

"Hold, Hercules," he said. "She is already a shade and you have nothing to fear from the dead."

"When has Hercules had anything to fear from either the living or the dead?" said the other spectre who had remained. And looking at him, Hercules saw that it was Meleager of Calydon, one of the Argonauts, who had been his shipmate on the quest for the Golden Fleece.

"Meleager!" he cried happily. "We are well met. I have not seen you since we parted company at Iolchos." And he tried to embrace him, but his hands met in the empty air.

"You can see me and we can talk," said Meleager, "but you cannot touch me, for I am but a shadow, insubstantial. What do you here in the Underworld?"

Hercules told him he had come to get Cerberus as one of his labours and Meleager nodded and said that if there was any man who could accomplish this it was Hercules. Then Hercules asked him if there was anything he could do for him when he returned to earth

"Yes," replied Meleager. "Take my greeting to my sister, Deianeira. Tell her that you have seen me and that I am as happy as a shade may be."

Hercules said he would do so, and noticed that Hermes looked at him strangely and smiled. Then he asked Meleager if there was anything else he could do for him, and Meleager said, "Well, we are hungry. We are always hungry."

"That is easily taken care of," said Hercules.

Some of Hades' cattle were grazing nearby. Selecting the largest and finest, Hercules killed it and cut its throat so that the ghosts could drink its blood. For this is the only food that ghosts can take and the reason for the sacrifices that men make to their memories.

At this Menoetes, Hades' herdsman, came hurrying up and said, "How dare you touch the king's cattle? You shall pay for it with your own life!" He threw himself on Hercules, gripping him with an iron grip.

Dropping his bow and club, Hercules broke the grip and they began to wrestle. Though Menoetes was tall as a Titan and almost as strong, Hercules took him around the middle, cracking his ribs. He picked him up and was about to dash him to the ground when a soft voice said, "The Underworld is full of ghosts, Hercules. We need no more of them. But we do need a herdsman to tend our cattle."

Turning, Hercules saw that the goddess Persephone, daughter of Demeter, had come out of the palace, accompanied by her husband, Hades, ruler of the Underworld.

"Are you asking for his life, O Queen?" asked Hercules.

"I am," she said.

"I will spare him if you will let me take your watchdog, Cerberus, to Eurystheus," said Hercules. "Since Eurystheus has a very tender heart, I do not think he will keep him long, but will let him return here to you."

Persephone glanced at her husband and Hades said, "If you can master him without your weapons, you can take him."

Hercules thanked him, set Menoetes down, and let him go. Then he and Hermes went over to the gate where Cerberus was chained. When the huge hound saw Hercules he began growling, and the serpents that formed his mane raised themselves up menacingly, and his tail with the poisoned sting curved over his back, prepared to strike.

"Release him," said Hercules. Hermes unchained him, and as the dog leaped at him, Hercules seized him by the throat—just below the point where it branched into three to support his three heads—and held him fast. Cerberus struck at Hercules with his poisoned sting, but the lion's skin protected him and he choked the huge hound until his growls turned to whines. When Hercules let him go, he slumped to the ground.

Saying goodbye to Persephone, Hades, and Meleager, Hercules half dragged, half carried Cerberus back to the river Styx. Charon was now more frightened of Hercules than ever, but he could not refuse Hermes, so he ferried both of them and the watchdog across to the other side, and they started up the long tunnel that led to the light of day.

They had gone some distance when they heard footsteps approaching and Hermes said, "Turn to the wall. Do not look."

Hercules obeyed, but as the shade passed by on its way to Tartarus, he caught a glimpse of it out of the corner of his eye. It seemed to be a woman, and though there was something familiar about her, her face was veiled and he could not tell who she was.

When she was gone they went on again and soon reached the upper world. Hercules thanked Hermes for his help and then set off for Mycenae, sometimes dragging Cerberus behind him and sometimes carrying him.

Hercules was right about Eurystheus. When the High King saw Cerberus he was terrified, even though he stood high above him on the city wall, and he told Hercules to turn him loose. Hercules did so, and the huge watchdog ran southward through the Peloponnese, barking furiously, and returned to his master in the Underworld. But the saliva that dripped from his three mouths as he ran gave rise to the poisonous plant called aconite.

"Do you agree," said Hercules as the barking of Cerberus died in the distance, "that I have completed all my twelve labours?"

"I do," said Eurystheus. "Go in peace."

"Thank you, great king," said Hercules, and raising his club in salute to him for the last time, he set off for Thebes.

He arrived there late in the afternoon when the streets were crowded. But instead of greeting him as they usually did with cheers and wreaths of flowers, the citizens of Thebes avoided him, turning away from him and hurrying into their houses.

Puzzled, Hercules went to the palace. Here too all drew back from him, dropping their eyes, until his brother, Iphicles, came into the great hall.

"Greetings, Iphicles," said Hercules. "Is the smell of the Underworld still so strong on me that all men avoid me?"

"That is not why they do so," said Iphicles gravely.

"If that is not why and you know the reason, tell me," said Hercules.

"I will," said Iphicles. "You have always been the bravest of men as well as the strongest. You will need all your courage and all your strength to endure the news I have for you. Your betrothed, Megara, is dead."

16

THE SLAVERY
OF HERCULES

"Dead?" said Hercules, staring at Iphicles. "She cannot be dead."

"But she is, my unfortunate brother."

"How did she die?"

"Of a fever just a few days ago. It took her suddenly at dusk and by morning she was dead."

What had happened was that Hera, more jealous of Hercules than ever now that he was about to complete his twelve labours, had struck at him in the only way that she could—by taking from him the woman he loved, the woman who should have been the reward for those labours.

Suddenly Hercules remembered the shape he had seen descending to the Underworld as he was returning from it—the veiled woman at whom Hermes had told him not to look—and he realized that this must have been Megara. He also remembered what he had said to her before he left for Mycenae for the last time: that none of the gods could be so heartless as to keep them apart after they had waited so long for one another.

With a roar like a wounded lion Hercules ran from the palace to the nearby temple of Zeus, and wild with rage, he tore the altar from its foundations, overturning it with a shattering crash. Then, putting his shoulder to one of the columns, he was about to bring it down—and with it the whole temple—when Zeus spoke to him in a voice of thunder.

"Hold, Hercules," he said. "Stay your hand!"

"Why should I stay my hand when you have done this cruel thing to me?" demanded Hercules.

"Because that is my commandment!"

Then, as Hercules hesitated, Zeus cast down a thunderbolt that made the temple blaze with light and shake like dice in a dice box.

"Does a son question his father?" said Zeus. "Does a man question a god? Does anyone question *me*? Man has his time on earth and his work. But what happens to him during his allotted days is not up to the gods, but up to the Fates, whom even the gods must obey."

"Even you?"

"Even I. It was not I who sent the fever to your betrothed. It was another. But since she was destined to die, there was naught I could do to change her fate. Now take this blow—this reminder that no one can have his will in all things—like the man you are."

"I will try, great Zeus," said Hercules, bowing his head. "Forgive me my rage."

"I will forgive you for it and for your impiety when you have made amends for it," said Zeus severely. "Then you shall have my favour again."

"What must I do to make amends?" asked Hercules.

"Go again to Delphi. The Oracle will tell you."

Slowly Hercules left the temple of Zeus. Iphicles was waiting for him and saw at once that his rage was over. Hercules did not tell him what had happened, but merely said he must go to Delphi, and Iphicles nodded.

So Hercules went again to the temple of Apollo, fasted, and was led down to the cave under the temple. Again the Pythoness appeared out of the darkness, sat on the throne set over the cleft in the earth, and breathed in the fumes that rose from it. Then, when the god had possessed her, she said, "Hercules, you have grievously offended Father Zeus by desecrating

his temple. To make amends, you must be sold into slavery for one year."

"Whose slave am I to be?" asked Hercules.

"The slave of Queen Omphale of Lydia," said the Pythoness.

"I hear and obey," said Hercules humbly.

He left the temple and found Hermes, who was the god of financial transactions as well as the guide of the souls of the dead, waiting for him.

"Now do you know why I told you not to look when we were returning from Tartarus?" said Hermes sympathetically.

Hercules nodded mutely.

"Look not so bleak," said Hermes. "There are still years of life ahead of you, and much joy. And, in the end, such glory and such a reward as no man has ever had before. But first there is the penance for your impiety."

Taking Hercules by the hand, he transported him to Ephesus in Asia Minor and offered him for sale in the marketplace as a nameless slave. Queen Omphale of Lydia was in the marketplace at the time, and though she did not know he was Hercules, she could see that he was an extraordinary man. As the oracle had foretold, she bought him.

Hercules served Queen Omphale faithfully for that

year, ridding her kingdom—as he had so many parts of Greece—of bandits, evildoers, and dangerous beasts. For instance, a giant of a man named Lityerses owned much land on the banks of the Maeander River. He would stop any traveller who came that way and force him to compete with him in reaping his fields. When he won, as he always did, he would cut off the traveller's head with his sickle and hide his body in the sheaves of grain. Hercules went to visit him and accepted his challenge. When he outreaped Lityerses, he served him as Lityerses had served others: he cut off his head and threw his body in the river.

Later on, when one of the Lydian cities revolted against the queen and marched on her capital, Hercules led her army against these enemies and routed them.

It was when he returned in triumph from this expedition that Omphale sent for him and said, "Who are you?"

"Your slave, O queen," said Hercules.

"You have served as my slave for almost a year, but the deeds that you have performed are not the deeds of a slave. They are the deeds of a great hero. And since you are Greek, you must be Hercules."

"A slave must answer to any name his master or mistress may choose to give him," said Hercules.

"Do not play games with me," said Omphale. "I

know that you are Hercules. Soon your year will be up and I will no longer be your mistress. But my feelings for you are such that I cannot bear to let you go. If you will stay on here you shall be, not my slave, but my husband and King of Lydia."

"You are not only kind and generous, but very beautiful," said Hercules, "and it is a hard thing for me to refuse you, but I am afraid I must. For I have a great longing to return to my native land."

Omphale sighed and said she had feared this would be his answer. But when his year of slavery was up she not only let him go but gave him many rich gifts as a token of her love and a reward for his great services to her.

Hercules decided to return home not by ship but by land, and so went north along the coast. When he neared Troy he saw the city gates were open and that a great crowd of Trojans had gathered about a rock that faced the sea. Approaching, he saw that all in the throng were weeping and saying farewell to a beautiful maiden who was chained to the rock. He asked who she was and was told that she was Hesione, daughter of Laomedon, King of Troy.

"But why are you chaining her to the rock?"

"Because we were advised to do so by the Oracle of Zeus Ammon," they told him. "Some months ago an enormous monster rose from the sea and came ashore, devouring men and cattle, laying the fields waste, and spreading a plague with his poisonous breath. Since then he has returned each day at noon. When we asked the oracle why this evil had been visited on us, we were told that King Laomedon had angered Poseidon and that the only way we could rid ourselves of it was if the king left his daughter here to be devoured by the monster."

"There is another and better way," said Hercules.

"What way is that?" they asked him.

"Take the princess back to Troy and I will deal with the monster," he said.

Though King Laomedon was eager to do this, his people were not, for they feared that no one, not even Hercules, could slay the monster. But going to the rock, Hercules broke the chains that bound Hesione, gave her over into her father's keeping, and told him to take her away. The Trojans still hesitated, but at that moment the monster appeared, and all those assembled there fled.

Raising his bow, Hercules loosed an arrow at the monster, but its scales were so hard that the arrow shattered. He shot two more arrows, but they did no more harm than the first.

Now the monster was almost ashore, and Hercules

saw that the Trojans had spoken the truth when they
said it was enormous. It was even larger than the Hydra
or the dragon that had guarded the apples of the Hesperides. He knew that his club would be useless against
it, and if its scales had shattered his arrows, they would
also turn his sword. There was only one way he could
kill it, and hoping that his year of slavery had restored
him to the favour of Zeus, he took that way.

When the monster opened its great jaws, Hercules
leaped over its teeth and, sword in hand, threw himself down its throat. He let himself be swallowed, then
struck out savagely with his sharp sword. The monster
turned and went back into the sea, writhing in agony
as Hercules slashed at its entrails. A few moments
later he had cut his way out through its unarmoured
belly and risen to the surface.

He swam away from the dying monster, and when
he reached the shore the Trojans greeted him as their
savior. King Laomedon, in gratitude, offered him Hesione as his bride. Hercules refused his offer with gra-
cious words but accepted as a gift two white horses
that had been given to Laomedon by Zeus—horses so
swift it was said they could run over water or over
standing corn. With these horses drawing his chariot,
Hercules left Troy and continued on his way home to
Greece.

17

DEIANEIRA

After he had left Troy, Hercules remembered the promise he had made in the Underworld to his old shipmate Meleager—a promise to take his greeting to Meleager's sister, Deianeira. Because of this—and because he did not wish to return to the place that could not help but remind him of Megara—instead of going to Thebes he went west to Calydon, in Aetolia.

Deianeira's father, King Oeneus, welcomed Hercules warmly when he arrived, for there was no one in Greece who did not know of him and his exploits. When Hercules asked for Deianeira, Oeneus told him she was not there but up in the hills, for Deianeira was a great huntress.

At sundown Deianeira returned to the palace, driving her own chariot. When Hercules saw her he caught his breath, for she was very beautiful—as beautiful as Megara if not more so. And as she threw the chariot reins to a stableboy, looking like the goddess Artemis coming home from the hunt, Hercules recalled something else: how Hermes had looked at him and smiled when Meleager had asked him to go see Deianeira— and he thought he knew why.

Hercules went up to Deianeira and said, "I bring you greetings."

"From whom?" she asked.

"From your brother, Meleager."

"But he is dead."

"Yes. It was his shade I saw in Tartarus. He asked me to bring you his greetings and tell you he is as happy as one can be who no longer walks the earth."

"I thank you for that message," she said. Then, sighing: "I have often wished that he were still alive, but I have never wished it more than I do now."

"Why is that?" asked Hercules.

Deianeira explained that during the past year many suitors had come to seek her hand, and the most pressing of them all had been the river-god Achelous. Deianeira had liked none of them, Achelous least of all. But since many of the suitors had been princes they had been so powerful and insistent that her father had not been able to hold out against them; he had finally agreed that they could compete among themselves in wrestling and that the winner should have Deianeira.

"Since Achelous is an immortal, he has defeated them all," she said. "And if, when he appears here tomorrow, no one challenges him, he will claim me. If Meleager were here, I think he might have been able to stand against him, but I do not know of anyone else who could."

"It might be that I could too," said Hercules. "Would that please you?"

"Nothing could please me more," she said, looking at him levelly. From the time she had first seen him, she had felt about him as he had about her.

"I am glad," said Hercules. "And I suspect that this is what your brother had in mind when he asked me to come here."

The next morning Achelous—huge, shaggy-bearded, and wearing green garments that shimmered like water—appeared at the palace.

"You know why I am here, O king," he said to Oeneus. "I have come to claim your daughter."

"I am afraid you cannot have her yet," said Oeneus. "There is one more suitor you must defeat before she can be yours."

"Who is that?" asked Achelous. And when Hercules stepped forward, he said, "You mean you are challenging me, Hercules?"

"I am."

"I have heard it said that you are something of a wrestler," said Achelous. "But I do not recall that you have ever matched your strength with an immortal."

"Antaeus may not have been a god," said Hercules, "but he was more than mortal. Still, you may be right. It may be that I have finally met my match. Let us see."

They went forth to the wrestling ground and took their positions, and when the signal was given they came at one another. Achelous took Hercules in a wet grip and tried to break his spine by bending him backward, as he had done to the other suitors before him. Hercules not only withstood him, but taking a deep breath and swelling his great chest, he broke his hold. Then he in turn took a grip on Achelous, and using both strength and skill, he tripped and threw him so that he landed heavily on his back. And so the first fall went to Hercules.

Achelous got to his feet scowling angrily, for he had never been thrown before. And when the signal was given for the second round of their match, he turned himself into a huge river serpent and wrapped

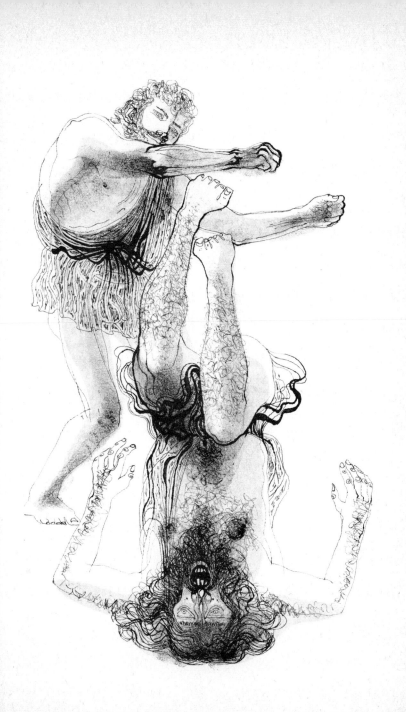

himself around Hercules, thinking to crush him in his powerful coils.

"You forget, Achelous, that I strangled serpents in my cradle," said Hercules. Freeing one hand he took him by the throat and gripped him so tightly that Achelous' senses left him and his coils loosened. Again Hercules threw him to the ground.

When Achelous had regained his senses and the signal was given for the last fall, he turned himself into another of his many shapes—that of a huge bull —and lowering his head, he charged at Hercules. But Hercules had also dealt with bulls before, and stepping nimbly aside he caught him by the horns. Putting forth all his strength, he threw the bull to the ground with such force that one of his horns was broken off. Mortally ashamed, the river-god did not transform himself back into his original shape, but still in the form of a bull—and a bull with only one horn—he ran from the wrestling ground.

Now Hercules approached the king and said, "Unless there are any others who would challenge me, it is now I who claim your daughter's hand."

"There are no others," said Oeneus. "And I cannot think of anyone to whom I would rather give her." Taking Deianeira's hand, he put it in that of Hercules.

And so Deianeira and Hercules were wed, and there

began the period of great happiness that Hermes had foretold. For Hercules loved her dearly, as she did him.

Some months later Hercules heard that Amphitryon, whom he still thought of as his father, and his mother, Alcmene, were staying with kinsmen of theirs in Trachis, which is on the far eastern side of Aetolia. Since Hercules had not seen them in some time and they had never met Deianeira, he decided to take his new bride to visit them.

About noon they came to the river Evenus, which was in full flood. As Hercules prepared to carry Deianeira over, the Centaur Nessus appeared and said, "I would consider it a great honour if you would permit me to carry your wife across, noble Hercules." Hercules looked at him narrowly, for he did not like Centaurs, and said, "Do you not think I can carry her over myself?"

"I do not think there is anything you cannot do," said Nessus. "But I think you will find it difficult to carry her and at the same time keep your weapons dry." Then, as Hercules still hesitated, he asked, "Do you not trust me? If you do not, then you cannot trust the gods, for it is they who appointed me to be the ferryman here."

"There is no one who has better reason to trust the gods than I," said Hercules. "Very well, then." And

placing Deianeira on the Centaur's back, he plunged
into the river and began to swim across, holding his
bow high.

Nessus waited until he was halfway over. Then,
pulling Deianeira from his back and holding her firmly
in his arms, he galloped away with her. For, like all
who had ever seen her, he had long loved her.

Deianeira screamed, and seeing what was happening, Hercules swam quickly back to shore. Nessus was
almost half a mile away by now, but raising his bow,
Hercules shot so skilfully that the arrow pierced the

Centaur's chest without so much as grazing Deianeira.

Nessus stumbled and fell, dropping Deianeira. From the way fire seemed to course through his every vein he knew he had been struck by one of the arrows that was poisoned by the Hydra's venom. And in that moment he thought of a way in which he could be revenged on Hercules.

"I am spent," he said to Deianeira. "And I deserve to die for having tried to run off with you. But let me make amends. Keep some of the blood from my wound, and if you ever have cause to doubt Hercules'

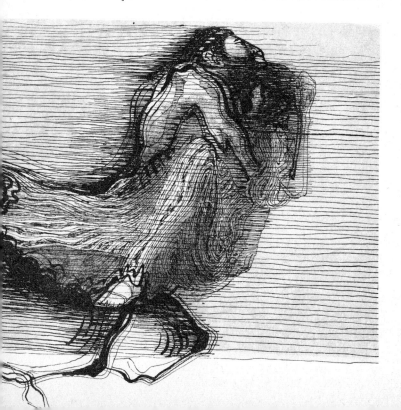

love for you, mix the blood with oil and anoint his shirt with it. From the time he puts it on he will never love another."

Then he fell dead.

Knowing how she herself felt about Hercules— and knowing how many other women had loved him —Deianeira hurriedly filled a jar with the Centaur's blood, sealed it, and hid it in her bosom before Hercules came running up. She said nothing about it to him, and this was to lead to Hercules' death.

18

THE DEATH
OF HERCULES

In the years that followed, Hercules and Deianeira had the children he had wanted for so long. There were five of them: four sons, who were as tall, strong, and brave as he was, and a daughter, who was as beautiful as Deianeira.

They were good years, the best of Hercules' life, but that life was now drawing to a close.

One summer when Hercules and Deianeira were staying with his kinsmen in Trachis, the city of Oechalia revolted and Hercules led an army against it. His eldest son, Hyllus, was now old enough to accompany him and acquitted himself well in the siege of that city.

When the city had fallen, Hercules made ready to celebrate the victory with a sacrifice of thanksgiving to Zeus. In preparation for this he sent his charioteer, Lichas, back to Trachis to ask Deianeira for his finest shirt and cloak, which he intended to wear while performing the ceremony. Now the King of Oechalia had a daughter named Iole who was very beautiful, and Deianeira became convinced that Hercules had fallen in love with her and intended to leave his wife for this much younger woman. Remembering what Nessus had said to her, she unsealed the jar that she had kept with her all this time, mixed the Centaur's blood with olive oil, and soaked Hercules' shirt in it. Then she put the shirt and cloak in a chest and told Lichas not to open it until Hercules was ready to wear the garments.

Lichas returned to Hercules, and Hercules put on the shirt first and then the cloak over it. He lit the fire on the altar and was throwing frankincense on it when he cried out in pain. The warmth of his body had brought out the poison in Nessus' blood, and it was searing his flesh like the flames that burned on the altar before him. He tried to rip off the shirt, but it was too late; his entire body felt as if it were on fire. He leaped into a nearby stream, but instead of easing the pain, the water only made it more intense: the stream has been scalding hot ever since and is still called Thermopylae, or the Hot Passage.

Now, though he was in agony, a great calm came over Hercules. Calling Hyllus to him, and several of his oldest companions, he led them to the peak of a nearby mountain and told them to build him a funeral pyre of oak and wild olive.

"You cannot die, father," said Hyllus, weeping.

"All men must die," said Hercules. "Even I who have been to the Underworld and returned from it. Now I can reveal to you a prophecy that was made to me many years ago by the Oracle of Zeus at Dodona. I was told that no man alive would ever kill me, but that a dead enemy would be my undoing. And so it has come to pass."

The pyre was now ready, and spreading his lion's skin out on top of it, Hercules lay down on the skin with his club as a pillow.

"Light the pyre," he ordered, but none of those with him would do so. Finally, however, a shepherd named Philoctetes put a torch to the huge pile of branches, and in gratitude Hercules gave him his bow, quiver, and arrows.

As the flames mounted higher and higher, Hercules looked up at the sky, and Zeus, proud of his favourite son's courage and fortitude, threw down a thunderbolt that consumed the pyre, turning it and the mortal remains of Hercules into ashes.

Deianeira did not outlive Hercules. For when she heard the news and realized that, indirectly, she had been responsible for his death, she killed herself.

But though that which was mortal of Hercules was gone, that which was immortal lived on. For true to the promise he had made before Hercules was born, Zeus brought him up to Olympus, where he became one with the other gods. As a god, he was accepted even by Hera; she adopted him as her son and came to love him as much as if he had been born to her and not to Alcmene.

Thus ends the tale of Hercules, the son of Zeus, who lived as a man, performed great feats during his days on earth, and after his death became a god.

GLOSSARY

Abderus (ab'-duh-rus). A skilled horse-tamer, who helped Hercules subdue the mares of Diomedes.

Achelous (ak-eh-lo'-us). A river-god, who wrestled with Hercules for the hand of Deianeira.

Adriatic Sea (ay-dri-at'-ik). An extension of the Mediterranean Sea, between the east coast of Italy and the west coasts of Yugoslavia and Albania.

Aegean Sea (ee-jee'-an). An extension of the Mediterranean Sea, bounded by Asia Minor in the east and Greece in the north and west.

Alcmene (alk-mee'-nee). Wife of King Amphitryon, and mother of Hercules by Zeus.

Amphitryon (am-fit'-ri-on). Exiled King of Mycenae and mortal husband of Hercules' mother.

Antaeus (an-tee'-us). King of Libya, born of Mother Earth, who won all his wrestling contests with strangers because he gained strength every time he touched the ground.

Apollo (a-pol′-o). God of light and healing.

Ares (air′-eez). God of war.

Artemis (ar′-te-mis). Virgin goddess of hunting and of wild animals.

Athene (a-thee′-nee). Goddess of wisdom and helper of heroes.

Atlas (at′-las). A giant forced by Zeus to support the heavens on his shoulders.

Augeias (aw-jee′-as). King of Elis, whose filthy stables Hercules had to clean.

Centaur (sen′-tawr). A creature that was half horse, half man.

Cerberus (ser′-ber-us). The three-headed watchdog who guarded the entrance to the Underworld.

Ceryneian hind (ser-i-nee′-yan). A lightning-swift deer, sacred to Artemis, caught by Hercules after a year's chase.

Charon (ker′-on). The ferryman who transported the dead across the river Styx into the Underworld.

Cnossus (nos′-us). A city in ancient Crete; the capital of King Minos.

Copreus (kop′-roos). The herald of King Eurystheus, who conveyed the High King's commands to Hercules.

Creon (Kree′-on). King of Thebes, the Greek city where Hercules was born.

Deianeira (dee-uh-nigh′-ra). Daughter of King Oeneus and sister of Meleager, who became the wife of Hercules.

Delphi (del′-figh). Site of the most famous Greek oracle, sacred to Apollo.

Diomedes (digh-o-mee′-deez). King of the Bistonians, whose man-eating horses Hercules had to capture.

Eleusinian Mysteries (ee-loo-sin′-i-yan). Ancient Greek religious rites that Hercules learned as a preparation for his descent into the Underworld.

Erginus (er-jigh′-nus). A king of Orchomenus, who conquered the Greek city of Thebes to avenge the death of his father in a chariot race.

Erymanthian boar (er-i-man′-thi-yan). A fierce beast that Hercules captured with the help of Artemis.

Eurystheus (you-ris′-thoos). High King of Mycenae and kinsman of Hercules, for whom he had to perform twelve labours.

Eurytion (you-rit′-i-on). The herdsman of King Geryon.

Geryon (jee-ree′-on). King of Tartessus, in Spain, whose famous cattle Hercules had to capture.

Hades (hay′-deez). King of the Underworld.

Hera (hee′-ra). The queen of heaven and wife of Zeus.

Hercules (her′-cue-leez). A Greek hero of tremendous strength, who performed twelve great labours and after his death became a god.

Hermes (her′-meez). Greek god. Messenger for the other gods.

Hesperides (hes-per′-i-deez). Daughters of Atlas, in whose garden grew the golden apples Hercules had to retrieve.

Hippolyte (hip-ol′-i-tee). Queen of the Amazons, whose golden belt Hercules had to retrieve.

Hyperboreans (high-per-bo′-ri-yans). The people who live at the back of the North Wind.

Iphicles (if′-i-kleez). The twin brother of Hercules.

Laomedon (lay-om′-e-don). King of Troy, whose daughter was rescued from a sea-monster by Hercules.

Megara (meg′-a-ra). The fiancée of Hercules.

Meleager (mel-ee-ay′-jer). Brother of Deianeira and a former shipmate of Hercules, whom he met again in the Underworld.

Minos (migh′-nos). King of Crete, whose realm Hercules freed of a destructive bull.

Mycenae (migh-seé-nee). An ancient Greek city in the Peloponnese, ruled by the High King.

Nemean lion (nee′-me-yan). A destructive beast killed by Hercules.

Nessus (nes′-us). A Centaur, half horse, half man, who gave Deianeira the poison that caused the death of Hercules.

Oeneus (ee′-noos). King of Calydon, and the father of Deianeira.

Olympus (o-lim′-pus). A mountain in Greece and the home of the gods.

Omphale (um-fa′-lee). Queen of Lydia whom Hercules served as a slave for one year after he had finished his twelve labours.

Orchomenus (or-komm′-eh-nus). A Greek city which received annual tribute from the city of Thebes until conquered by Hercules.

Peloponnese (pel′-o-puh-nees′). The southern peninsula of Greece, attached to the mainland by the Isthmus of Corinth.

Persephone (per-sef′-on-nee). Queen of the Underworld.

Perseus (per′-soos). A heroic ancestor of Hercules, famed for killing the Gorgon Medusa, whose head had turned all who looked on it to stone.

Pillars of Hercules. Two large columns built by Hercules—one in Europe and the other in Africa—where the waters of the Mediterranean Sea mingle with those of the Atlantic Ocean.

Poseidon (Po-sigh'-don). God of the sea.

Stymphalian birds (stim-fay'-li-yan). Man-eating birds that Hercules had to drive away as one of his labours.

Tartarus (tar'-ta-rus). The Underworld.

Teiresias (tigh-ree'-si-as). The most famous soothsayer in Greece when Hercules was a child.

Thebes (theebz). An ancient Greek city, where Hercules was born, and also the city he founded in Egypt.

Thermopylae (ther-mop'-i-lee). The stream made permanently hot when Hercules jumped in to escape the burning poison of his garment. A narrow pass nearby was the site of a famous Greek battle with the Persians.

Thespius (thes'-pi-us). The king whose cattle were killed by the Nemean lion and who helped purify Hercules after his madness.

Triple Goddess. The Great Mother Goddess of the Mediterranean basin, who was known by many names. The island of Samothrace was sacred to her.

Zeus (zoos). Supreme ruler of the gods.

More Beaver Books

We hope you have enjoyed this Beaver Book. Here are some of the other titles:

A Knight and his Castle What it was like to live in a castle, by R. Ewart Oakeshott

Travel Quiz A brain-teasing quiz book for all the family on all aspects of travel by plane, train and car

My Favourite Animal Stories Sad, funny and exciting stories about all sorts of animals, chosen and introduced by Gerald Durell

Who Knows? Twelve unsolved mysteries involving sudden death, mysterious disappearances and hidden treasure, by Jacynth Hope-Simpson

The Call of the Wild The epic story of Buck the great sledge dog in the frozen North, by Jack London

The Last of the Vikings Henry Treece's exciting story, in the saga tradition, about the young Harald Hardrada, King of Norway; with more superb illustrations by Charles Keeping

Ghost Horse Dramatic story about a legendary stallion in the American West, by Joseph E. Chipperfield

New Beavers are published every month and if you would like the *Beaver Bulletin* – which gives all the details – please send a stamped addressed envelope to:

Beaver Bulletin
The Hamlyn Group
Astronaut House
Feltham
Middlesex TW14 9AR

387372